CEREBROSPINAL FLUID

CLINICAL BIOCHEMISTRY, PHYSIOLOGY AND DIAGNOSTIC CHARACTERISTICS

NEUROLOGY - LABORATORY AND CLINICAL RESEARCH DEVELOPMENTS

Additional books in this series can be found on Nova's website
under the Series tab.

Additional e-books in this series can be found on Nova's website
under the e-book tab.

NEUROLOGY - LABORATORY AND CLINICAL
RESEARCH DEVELOPMENTS

CEREBROSPINAL FLUID

CLINICAL BIOCHEMISTRY, PHYSIOLOGY AND DIAGNOSTIC CHARACTERISTICS

LAWRENCE E. KEEN
EDITOR

New York

For permission to use material from this book please contact us:
Telephone 631-231-7269; Fax 631-231-8175
Web Site: http://www.novapublishers.com

NOTICE TO THE READER

Library of Congress Cataloging-in-Publication Data

ISBN: 978-1-63117-908-2

Library of Congress Control Number: 2014938429

Published by Nova Science Publishers, Inc. † New York

Contents

Preface   **vii**

Chapter 1   CSF Biomarkers: Review of the literature
                  and Critical Appraisal in Spinal Cord Injury   **1**
                  *Tristan Fried, George M. Ghobrial
                  and James S. Harrop*

Chapter 2   Cerebrospinal Fluid: Novel Developed Biomarkers
                  in Neurological Disease   **15**
                  *M. Dessi, F. Duranti, M. Pieri, G. Sancesario,
                  R. Zenobi and S. Bernardini*

Chapter 3   Cerebrospinal Fluid Biochemical Markers
                  of Cerebral Metabolism in Dogs   **61**
                  Alba Galán and Beatrice E. Carletti

Chapter 4   Cerebrospinal Fluid: Guidance for the Selection
                  and Interpretation of Laboratory Tests   **75**
                  *Karina Rodríguez-Capote, Vilte E. Barakauskas,
                  Mathew P. Estey and Trefor N. Higgins*

Index   **107**

Preface

The cerebrospinal fluid (CSF) is a dynamic, metabolically active fluid that occupies the subarachnoid space and the ventricular system around the brain, and has many important functions. CSF is a promising body fluid for the search of biomarkers associated with neurological disease, because the CSF has more physical contact with brain than any other fluids, biochemical changes related to many pathology may be reflected in the CSF. Although CSF is obtained by lumbar puncture, invasive and potentially painful for the patient, it is probably the most informative fluid in biomarkers discovery for neurological disease prognosis. This book discusses CSF biomarkers; novel developed biomarkers in neurological diseases; CSF biochemical markers of cerebral metabolism in dogs; and guidance for the selection and interpretation of laboratory tests.

Chapter 1 - Spinal cord injury (SCI) affects over 10,000 Americans annually, leaving patients in a severely disabled state, left with very few therapeutic interventions to improve their quality of life. One overlooked diagnostic test is the use of cerebrospinal fluid (CSF) biomarkers as a prognostication tool for SCI to supplement outdated classification systems for SCI that have largely remain unchanged. Prior work has shown increasing concentrations of neural protein biomarkers such as S100b, Tau, and GFAP with a correlation with an increasing severity of SCI by ASIA classification. The glial cell derived marker S-100 has been previously implicated in neuronal damage, particularly in spinal cord injury and traumatic brain injury(TBI). Further studies have shown S100 to be also elevated in stroke [6] in both peripheral blood and CSF. Studies have shown the specificity of S100 for the central nervous system. Only in the setting of cord injury, did investigators observe a five-fold increase in S100 levels. In the setting of isolated lumbar nerve root and plexus avulsions, no elevation occurred. All CSF biomarkers studied in SCI are seen to elevate in the setting of concomitant TBI. Neuron Specific Enolase (NSE) is a neural enzyme shows a peak at 6 hours after spinal cord injury. Given this ideal timing, further studies are aimed at quantification of NSE levels for use as a prognosticating factor. A positive correlation with severity of injury had been shown in animal models as well as human studies of aortic cross-clamping for cardiac surgery. Glial fibrillary acid protein (GFAP) and neuronal filament light chain (NFL) are also detected in SCI, but are the least specific markers to CNS injury.

Chapter 2 - The cerebrospinal fluid (CSF) is a dynamic, metabolically active fluid that occupies the subarachnoid space and the ventricular system around the brain, and has many important functions. CSF is a promising body fluid for the search of biomarkers associated with neurological disease, because CSF has more physical contact with brain than any other fluid, and biochemical changes related to many pathologies may be reflected in the CSF.

Although CSF is obtained by lumbar puncture, invasive and potentially painful for the patient, it is probably the most informative fluid in biomarkers discovery for neurological disease prognosis. Basic CSF diagnostics tests, such as the CSF/serum albumin ratio and CSF cell counts, have been used to diagnose inflammatory and infectious CNS disorders in adults and children for decades. The use of biomarkers is increasingly proposed as a method to refine the diagnosis and guide the treatment of numerous diseases. In this chapter, the authors review the development of candidate biomarkers in CSF and serum for different pathologies. The authors focus on established biomarkers, those that have been evaluated in several studies by different research groups, and the authors discuss their implementation in clinical routines and their potential role in clinical trials.

Besides the state of art about what is known on classical CSF biomarkers for early diagnosis in routine clinical practice, there also are international research initiatives aimed at identifying new biomarkers for detection, and monitoring of pathological processes in the brain. Recently biomarkers are useful in detecting the preclinical as well as the symptomatic stages of Alzheimer Disease (AD). The core CSF biomarkers total tau (T-tau), phosphorylated tau (P-tau) and the 42 amino acid form of b-amyloid (Ab42) reflect AD pathology, and are highly accurate in diagnosing AD with dementia and prodromal AD in mild cognitive impairment cases. Among recognized mediators, other new methods and tests can help highlight inflammatory or neurodegenerative processes in the CNS, accumulating evidence indicates that interleukin-6 (IL-6) is a new potential marker of CNS diseases. Another new test specific to diagnosing multiple sclerosis (MS) is the nephelometric assay for k free light chain determination and kFLC Index calculation in cerebrospinal fluid and serum. Only the CSF oliglonal band and IgG index are currently used to assist with MS diagnosis. The new nephelometric test may be a useful procedure for detection, potentially for monitoring intrathecal immunoglobulin synthesis, and to permit a rapid discriminatory diagnosis of MS.

In this chapter, the authors discuss the recent advancements of clinical diagnostic CSF tests with particular emphasis on possible new biomarkers for monitoring the early development of CNS disease before significant cognitive dysfunction and also to stratify clinical prognosis.

Finally the rationale for the use of CSF biomarkers to identify and monitor the mechanism of action of new drug candidates is also outlined in this chapter.

Chapter 3 - Alterations in CSF levels of different neurotransmitters, enzymes and neuronal metabolic substrates have been found in different diseases affecting the central nervous system in dogs and cats. CSF lactate, pyruvate and lactate/pyruvate ratio have been proposed as biomarkers of brain energy metabolism in humans and dogs. A recent study describes mean pyruvate (0.057 mM/l [0.01-0.151 mM/l]), and lactate (1.189 mM/l [0.416 – 1.850 mM/l]) concentration and L/P ratio (44.247 [6.110-161.00]) in 18 healthy dogs. In this study, no correlation was found between CSF lactate and pyruvate concentrations and serum lactate and pyruvate concentrations, CSF lactate and pyruvate concentrations and TNCC and CSF lactate and pyruvate concentrations and anesthetic time.

Traditionally, changes in concentration of these metabolites have been observed when oxidative damage, brain hypoxia or mitochondrial damage is present. However, recently, lactate has been considered a central neuroprotective agent. In addition, lactate serves as a critical neuronal energy substrate with positive vasodilatory effects. Increased amounts of CSF pyruvate and lactate have been found in human patients with Alzheimer's disease (AD) and vascular dementia, and in dogs with Canine Cognitive Dysfunction (CCD). An impaired cerebral oxidative glucose metabolism has been suspected in these contexts. It has been reported that antioxidant enriched diet leads to easier learning and memory improvements in dogs, and that it may be beneficial for promoting a physiologic brain aging and reducing the risk of neurodegenerative disease. Influence of antioxidant on CSF composition has been suggested in a study evaluating healthy dogs CSF after 50 days of treatment with nutraceutical compounds. CSF biochemical variables such as sodium and glucose concentration were significantly increased after treatment, while lactate concentration and L/P ratio were significantly decreased. Considering that lactate concentration in the brain is dependent upon its rate of production and independent of the blood lactate concentration, the elevation of CSF glucose in the face of significantly lower lactate concentrations may reflect a brain energy metabolism improvement after nutraceutical administration.

Chapter 4 - Examination of cerebrospinal fluid (CSF) provides important diagnostic information in a number of infectious and noninfectious disorders of the central nervous system (CNS). Rather than presenting a comprehensive overview of CSF composition, physiology and changes seen in disease, the focus of this chapter will be on providing some guidance in the selection and interpretation of laboratory tests associated with a variety of neurological conditions.

Biochemical tests such as protein and glucose are performed routinely to complement macroscopic, microscopic and cytological analysis in the diagnosis of acute CNS infections. Other tests are performed in specific clinical situations, for example, detection of bilirubin to rule in/out subarachnoid hemorrhage or immunoglobulin quantitation with evaluation of oligoclonal bands in the diagnostic workup of multiple sclerosis. CSF specific proteins such as beta-2-transferrin and beta trace protein can be measured to identify CSF leakage. The last section of this chapter will discuss some emerging CSF markers with potential utility in the diagnosis of neurodegenerative diseases such as Alzheimer disease (tau protein and amyloid beta-42).

In: Cerebrospinal Fluid
Editor: Lawrence E. Keen

ISBN: 978-1-63117-908-2
© 2014 Nova Science Publishers, Inc.

Chapter 1

CSF Biomarkers: Review of the literature and Critical Appraisal in Spinal Cord Injury

Tristan Fried[1], George M. Ghobrial[1] and James S. Harrop[2]*

[1]Department of Neurological Surgery, Thomas Jefferson University Hospital, Philadelphia, PA, US
[2]Neurological Surgery and Orthopedic Surgery
Thomas Jefferson University Hospital, Philadelphia, PA, US

Abstract

Spinal cord injury (SCI) affects over 10,000 Americans annually, leaving patients in a severely disabled state, left with very few therapeutic interventions to improve their quality of life. One overlooked diagnostic test is the use of cerebrospinal fluid (CSF) biomarkers as a prognostication tool for SCI to supplement outdated classification systems for SCI that have largely remain unchanged. Prior work has shown increasing concentrations of neural protein biomarkers such as S100b, Tau, and GFAP with a correlation with an increasing severity of SCI by ASIA classification. The glial cell derived marker S-100 has been

* Corresponding author: James Harrop, MD, Professor of Neurological Surgery and Orthopedic Surgery, Thomas Jefferson University Hospital, Email: James.Harrop@jefferson.edu.

previously implicated in neuronal damage, particularly in spinal cord injury and traumatic brain injury (TBI). Further studies have shown S100 to be also elevated in stroke [6] in both peripheral blood and CSF. Studies have shown the specificity of S100 for the central nervous system. Only in the setting of cord injury, did investigators observe a five-fold increase in S100 levels. In the setting of isolated lumbar nerve root and plexus avulsions, no elevation occurred. All CSF biomarkers studied in SCI are seen to elevate in the setting of concomitant TBI. Neuron Specific Enolase (NSE) is a neural enzyme shows a peak at 6 hours after spinal cord injury. Given this ideal timing, further studies are aimed at quantification of NSE levels for use as a prognosticating factor. A positive correlation with severity of injury had been shown in animal models as well as human studies of aortic cross-clamping for cardiac surgery. Glial fibrillary acid protein (GFAP) and neuronal filament light chain (NFL) are also detected in SCI, but are the least specific markers to CNS injury.

Keywords: Cerebrospinal fluid biomarker, spinal cord injury, translational research

Introduction

Spinal cord injury (SCI) affects over 10,000 Americans annually, [4] potentially leaving patients in a severely disabled state, and unfortunately there are very few therapeutic interventions to improve their quality of life. With greater than 50% of spinal cord injuries losing both motor and sensation distal to the injury, also referred to as being complete, effective interventions leading to improvement have been sparse. Despite the large number of scientific publications in the field of SCI research, little translational impact in the clinical setting has been made. Standardization and specialty institutions for spine care have made the biggest impact on improving patient's quality of life. While promising new therapies such as cell-based transplantation are being investigated as an intervention for spinal cord injury, one overlooked potential area of research is cerebrospinal fluid (CSF) biomarkers which may serve as a prognostication tool and potential therapeutic intervention in SCI.

One difficulty with treating SCI patients is that the neurological examination is felt to be unreliable within the acute injury period and thus difficult to use as a prognosticating tool. Presently, MRI offers the most helpful assessment of the degree of SCI with findings such as spinal cord hemorrhage and expansive lesion length to carry a relatively worse prognosis.

The difficulty with clinical grading and classification systems for SCI is that they have remain unchanged in the past few decades. [13] Recently, new animal and human studies have described CSF biomarker profiles in the setting of spinal cord hypoxia and traumatic injury. [11, 23] CSF biomarkers were initially discovered and investigated in traumatic brain injury (TBI). This information and markers were then applied to traumatic SCI. It is believed that these biomarkers in the CSF may serve as a useful adjunct to radiographic imaging and clinical exam in the prognosis of SCI. [11, 12, 15]

In impact sports often there is difficulty in determining transient injuries to the spinal cord with brachial plexus trauma. These brachial plexus injuries or often interchangeably called 'stingers', are the result a stretch injury to the proximal cervical nerve root or plexus. [21] This condition was seen roughly once in every 100,000 football players, with an increasing incidence with the advancement to prestigious levels of play. While the pathophysiology of this injury is not felt to be a SCI, the use of biomarkers might be able to aid in quantitatively assessing the severity of this scenario. As with the collection of CSF biomarkers in sports related TBI, the use of this information may provide for a predictive model. In traumatic SCIs this information could be implemented and be incorporated into return to play guidelines for spinal injuries.

The first biomarkers detected were neurofilament light chain (NFL) and glial fibrillary acid protein (GFAP) by Guez and colleagues in 2003. [7] Subsequently biomarkers have expanded to include numerous proteins whose clinical significance have yet to be fully elucidated. Work by Kwon et al. demonstrated increasing concentrations of neural protein biomarkers S-100beta, Tau, and GFAP with increasing severity of SCI by ASIA classification. [12] The authors provide an in depth review of the current literature regarding the potential use of CSF biomarkers as a prognosticating factor for SCI.

Biomarkers Specificity in the Setting of Spinal Cord Injury and Nerve Root Injury S100-B

The glial cell-derived marker S-100 beta has been previously implicated in neuronal damage, particularly in spinal cord injury and traumatic brain injury (TBI). This marker is not permeable to the blood brain barrier (BBB), and therefore not normally found in the serum. [5] In TBI, injury to the BBB is not unexpected, and hence these markers can be found in both serum and CSF.

Several studies have shown S100 beta to be also elevated in stroke [6] in both peripheral blood and CSF. [3, 5, 9, 10] Ma and colleagues [16] evaluated CSF markers of S-100 beta in the setting of SCI alone, isolated lumbar nerve root and lumbar plexus avulsions, and combination injuries. Only in the setting of SCI, did investigators observe a five-fold increase in S100 beta concentration from patient baselines. These increases in S100 beta were not observed with nerve root injury in the absence of SCI. However, in theory, in the setting of concomitant TBI, it would be difficult to discern which organ is contributing to the greatest flux in S100 beta level.

Neuron Specific Enolase

Neuron Specific Enolase (NSE) is a neural enzyme confined to the neural lineage and tends to have a peak concentration in the CSF at 6 hours after spinal cord injury. [12] Therefore, this timing may prove to be useful as a prognosticating factor aimed at quantification of NSE levels and degree of SCI as NSE can be monitored on the day of hospital admission. Work by Cao and colleagues have illustrated that the elevation in NSE increases with the severity of SCI. [3] Loy et al. [14] reported elevations of 2.3 and 3.1 fold correlating with increasing severity of injury (from 150 to 200 kilodyns, (P<0.001) respectively). Khaladj et al. [9], in a similar model of aortic cross-clamping, demonstrated the link between CSF NSE concentrations and spinal cord ischemia with peak elevations at 6h.

GFAP

Glial fibrillary acidic protein (GFAP) is a monomeric intermediate protein located only within the central nervous system. GFAP is found in the astroglial skeleton and was first described as an acidic protein isolated from fibrous astrocytes by Eng in 1971. [14] Therefore, it is thought that it might be a useful biomarker for neurodegenerative disorders as well as cerebrovascular accidents and severe TBI. [13] In addition, GFAP has also been shown to be elevated after ischemic spinal cord injuries. [15]

NFL

Neurofilament light chain (NFL), also known as neurofilament light polypeptide is a cytoskeletal component in nerve axons. The neurofilament hetropolymer consists of light, medium, and heavy chains. It is believed that proteolysis of neurofilaments occurs in axonal injury, resulting in the increased neurofilament light chain that has been observed with nerve cell death. [13] Prior work has shown the specificity of NFL to axonal injury. [19,12] In rat SCI studies by Kang, Upregulation of neuronal filaments has been observed in the CSF with a maximal window between 6 and 24 hours after SCI. [8] Because of the elevation of heavy chain neurofilaments in the serum seen in TBI, neurofilament markers are relatively less ideal to follow in the setting of concomitant TBI and SCI. [1]

Methods

A MEDLINE database search was conducted for relevant abstracts from 1970 to present (December 2013). Keywords and MeSH specifically included "cerebrospinal fluid (or CSF) and biomarkers". Papers were limited to English and included both published and manuscripts published before print. After a manual search of the abstracts and titles, relevant papers were then fully reviewed and graded by two authors (G.G., T.F.). Those articles of particular relevance and interest were then investigated for relevant references. Finally, all articles were evaluated for inclusion by the remaining authors.

Inclusion and Exclusion Criteria

Case series, comparative cohort studies, all clinical trials, reviews, and meta-analyses were considered eligible. Articles must have also been found to address pertinent clinical questions, either in part, or in whole.

Abstracts evaluated for exclusion were non-comparative and descriptive studies, technical notes, and case reports. Exclusion criteria included articles that were unrelated to the interventions or outcomes of interest.

Data Extraction and Analysis

Grading of articles on quality of evidence for human studies was done via the Oxford Center for Evidence-Based Medicine (CEBM) ranking criteria. [16]

Results

S-100 Beta

The most commonly studied CSF biomarker related to traumatic SCI was found to be S-100 beta. It was identified in prospectively collected, non-randomized non-controlled, human studies as well as animal studies (Table 1). Of these studies, five were animal based, while eight were focused on human patients. Most studies demonstrated a correlation between an elevation in the S-100 beta protein and the presence of a traumatic SCI. In addition, Skouen and colleagues observed a tendency for S-100 beta in pigs to correlate with the severity of nerve root injury compared to control (p=0.05). [20]

Numerous studies have characterized the temporal concentrations of S-100 beta. Ma and coinvestigators tested serum levels in 144 rat subjects at 3, 12, and 72 hours after a traumatically induced SCI and reported an increased S-100 beta concentration linearly with this time (p<0.05). [16] At 72 hours, a peak concentration was reached that was 5 times greater compared to controls. The S-100 beta levels remained elevated for 6 days after the injury before returning to baseline. Cao [4] tested serum and CSF in 80 adult male rats randomly separated into groups by injury severity. Both serum and CSF sampling performed at regular intervals found significant CSF increases at 2 hours with respect to serum concentrations as well as reaching a peak concentration at 6 hours (p<0.05). [20] Loy et al. [14] performed spinal contusions on 34 adult rat specimens and obtained serum sampling at either 6 or 24 hours. At 6 hours, a peak was observed in which there was a significant difference from the sham (p<0.05) and controls (p=0.01).

Our understanding of the S-100 beta protein concentration profile has been furthered from the results of prospectively collected data from human aortic aneurysm surgery. Van Dogen [22] completed a study in 8 humans who underwent thoracoabdominal aortic aneurysm repair (TAAA). Serum and CSF biomarker measurements were made before thoracic aorta cross-clamping, during the cross- clamping of the critical aortic segment, as well as five minutes after reperfusion, during skin closure, and 24 hours postoperative. The serum concentrations of S100 beta remained constant. However, the CSF values peaked five minutes after reperfusion. Of the 8 patients, 1 became paraplegic and the CSF values for that individual continued to rise to a peak at 24 hours. [22]

Table 1. S100b, Review of the Current Literature

Study	Serum /CSF	Peak Time	Animal/ human	Level of evidence	Comment
Skouen	CSF	1 w	Pigs	n/a	Increased (p=0.05)
Ma	Serum	3, 12, and 72 hours	Rat	n/a	Increased level (p<0.05)
Loy	Serum	6h	Rat	n/a	Increased s100b (p<0.05) for sham and (p=0.01) control
Cao	Both	6h	Rat	n/a	Serum and CSF elevated (p<0.05)
Van Dongen	Both	5 m after AAA repair /24 hours post SCI	human	prospective (III)	CSF peak during surgery. Remained elevated in paraplegia.
Van Dongen	CSF	5 m after AAA	human	prospective (III)	CSF increased during the procedure for all patients.
Kunihara	Both	48 h post surgery	human	prospective (III)	Increased levels (p<0.01) in four patients with SCI
Marquardt	Serum	9d post	human	prospective (III)	In MESCC, significantly elevated marker in nonambulatory group.
Marquardt	Serum	3-5d post surgery	human	prospective (III)	Increased level in unfavorable outcome (p<0.003)
Winnerkvist	CSF	2 d post surgery	human	prospective (II)	Elevated levels (p<0.05) in five patients with post operative SCI.
Khaladj	Both	6 h post surgery	human	prospective (III)	Significantly increased in SCI incurred during surgery.

In a second study by Van Dogen [23], 19 human patients underwent CSF diagnostic testing after elective TAAA. CSF samples were taken in the previous fashion: after induction, during cross clamping, 5 minutes after reperfusion, during skin closure and 24 hours post operatively. Intraoperative transcranial electrical stimulation (TES) decreased during the procedure correlated with an increase in S-100 beta protein concentration. CSF increased for all patients and reached a peak five minutes after reperfusion as seen in the prior study. [23]

In a study by Kunihara, [10] 23 humans underwent elective TAAA surgery. Both serum and CSF samples were collected before the operation, at 0 hours, 6 hours, 12 hours, 18 hours, 24 hours, 48 hours, and 72 hours after the operation. Patients with postoperative paralysis had increased S-100 beta in the CSF ($p<0.0001$) compared to those not paralyzed and reached a peak at 48 hours postoperatively. [10] Winnerkvist [24] studied S-100 beta CSF concentrations in 39 human subjects undergoing TAAA surgery. Of those, 5 had postoperative SCI. The mean increase in S-100 beta in this subgroup had an 18-fold peak during the second day after surgery ($p<0.05$). [24] Khaladj [9] and colleagues tested patients who underwent TAAA surgery. 13 patients had both serum and CSF concentrations collected at baseline before, during, after clamping and then 7 subsequent times over a three day postoperative period. In 2 of 13 patient, a significantly higher peak was seen in those with a documented SCI at 6 hours after surgery ($p<0.001$). [9]

S-100 beta profiles have also been characterized in SCI due to less common etiologies. Marquardt [18] completed a study that examined 34 patients with paresis due to metastatic epidural spinal cord compression (MESCC). Serum samples were taken every day for ten days. In those patients who had a favorable outcome, and were ambulatory, the serum concentrations steadily decreased while a significant elevation was seen in the nonambulatory group ($p=0.0001$). Another study by Marquardt [17] looked at the effects of spinal cord compression due to epidural empyema. The peak concentration was met at 2 days and returned to baseline after 3 days while in the nonambulatory group the elevated S-100 beta concentrations persisted beyond the third day. ($p<0.003$). [25]

NSE

Neuron Specific Enolase (NSE) although studies less than S-100 beta, has been previously characterized in CSF animal studies. Loy [14] in a rat SCI study found serum samples taken at 6 or 24 hours to have an increased NSE serum level for contusions as high as 2.3 times the baseline value in 150 kdyn contusions ($p<0.001$) and even higher to 3.1 times baseline for 200-kdyne contusions ($p<0.001$). Cao [4] found NSE concentrations in both the serum and the CSF to be elevated in rats by 2 hours after injury ($p<0.05$) peaking at 6 hours. Moderate and severely injured rats had higher elevations ($p<0.05$).

In a study by Brisby [2], 15 humans with sciatica and lumbar disc herniation were compared to control patient without this ailments. Overall, no significant change in the NSE biomarker was noted (Table 2).

Table 2. Neuron Specific Enolase, Review of the Current Literature

Study	Serum/ CSF	Biomarker Time Course	animal/ human	Level of evidence	comment
Skouen	CSF	none	Pigs	n/a	No significant difference
Loy	Serum	6 hours after sci	Sprague-dawley rats	n/a	NSE levels increased ($p<0.001$)
Cao	Both	6 hours after sci	Sprague-dawley rats	n/a	Elevated ($p<0.05$)
Brisby	CSF	none	Humans	prospective (III)	No significant difference

Table 3. N- filament Light Chain, Review of the Current Literature

Study	Serum/ CSF	Biomarker Time Course	animal/ human	Level of evidence	comment
Skouen	CSF	none	Pigs	n/a	1 week after injury nfl elevated ($p<0.001$)
Guez	CSF	unknown	Humans	prospective with control (IV)	Increase
Winnerkvist	CSF	3 days after AAA surgery	Humans	prospective (II)	Elevated to ($p<0.01$)
Brisby	CSF	unknown	Humans	prospective (III)	Increased four fold ($p<0.01$)

GFAP

Skouen studied GFAP protein CSF concentrations in SCI finding no significant changes in concentration. [20] However, Guez [7] studied 23 human patients with cervical SCI. They found significantly increased GFAP concentrations within the CSF of the most severely injured.

Winnerkvist [24] in an analysis after TAAA surgery, CSF levels of GFAP showed significant increases on the first day (p<0.001), later peaking on day three (Table 3).

NFL

Skouen found elevations of NFL to be greater than sham and the control in his aforementioned biomarker analysis (p<0.001). [17] While Brisby found NSE to not be helpful as a marker for nerve injury in sciatica or acute lumbar disc herniations, he found a 4 fold increase in the concentration of NFL (p<0.01) versus controls. [4] Similarly, Guez found NFL to be markedly elevated in cervical cord injury (Table 4). [3]

Discussion

As seen above, understanding in the field of biomarkers for SCI severity has seen significant advances in the past twenty years. There is potential in CSF diagnostics to assist medical examinations adjunctively in the grading of spinal cord injury severity where other methods fall short. A growing body of evidence has shown a positive correlation between the presence of SCI and injury severity (Table 5).

Structurally, with future clinicopathologic work, biomarkers will show distinct advantages over expensive diagnostic imaging such as MRI as they will be more specific for tissue destruction, therefore able to distinguish between edema and cellular necrosis not often apparent on MRI. Moreover, a combination of imaging and adjunctive biomarkers can potentially yield more specific physiologic data than traditional imaging. [13] This has already been partially realized through significant correlative studies of neurophyisiologic monitoring, SCI, and CSF biomarker elevations in work by van Dongen. [9]

Table 4. Glial Fibrillary Acid Protein, Review of the Current Literature

Study	Serum / CSF	Biomarker Time Course	animal/ human	Level of evidence	comment
Skoen	CSF	none	Pigs	n/a	No significant difference
Guez	CSF	unknown	Humans	prospective (IV)	Increased
Winnerkvist	CSF	3 days after TAAA surgery	Humans	prospective (II)	Increased to (p<0.001) in 5 patients with SCI

Table 5. Comparison of CSF Biomarkers

Biomarkers	N, studies	Source	Peak Time	Advantages	Disadvantages
S100 beta	11	Cytoplasm, nucleus. Abundant in glial and neural cells.	5 m- 72 h	Most widely studied.	Not specific.
NSE	4	Cytoplasm of neurons. Upregulated in damaged axons. Present RBCs and platelets.	6 h	Relatively specific.	Limited in traumatic SCI.
NFL	4	A cytochemical component of axons. Localized to soma and axons.	72 h	nerve specific .	Confounded results during TBI state.
GFAP	3	It is in the astroglial skeleton.	72 h	Confined to CNS.	Confounded results during TBI state.

Even with these potential advantages there are still some major issues with this method of assessment. The primary issue is the specificity of these molecules. The two most common molecules studied and used to find the presence and severity of SCI is the S-100 beta and the NSE. These molecules are not very specific as they are found in many types of nerve tissue and may be present during TBI experienced at the same time as SCI. [19] Timing is another major concern, as biomarkers show a considerable variation in peak concentrations (Table 5). This problem issue will be further resolved with future studies so time based curves can be utilized for clinical comparison.

Finally there are only four biomarkers presented here for study. Since these markers are limited by their specificity, more study is needed before they can become a useful adjunct in SCI monitoring and prognosis.

Conclusion

CSF biomarkers can potentially be useful in grading the severity of SCI severity. The current studies are predominantly nonhuman studies, and a small proportion are nonrandomized human studies. Larger, prospective, randomized studies are needed to understand the impact that CSF biomarkers could potentially have in SCI prognostication.

References

[1]   Anderson, K. J., Scheff, S. W., Miller, K. M., Roberts, K. N., Gilmer, L. K. et al. (2008). The phosphorylated axonal form of the neurofilament subunit NF-H (pNF-H) as a blood biomarker of traumatic brain injury. *Journal of neurotrauma*, 25(9), 1079-1085.

[2]   Brisby, H., Olmarker, K., Rosengren, L., Cederlund, C. G. & Rydevik, B. (1999) Markers of nerve tissue injury in the cerebrospinal fluid in patients with lumbar disc herniation and sciatica. *Spine*, 24(8), 742-746.

[3]   Cao, F., Yang, X. F., Liu, W. G., Hu, W. W., Li, G., et al. (2008). Elevation of neuron-specific enolase and S-100beta protein level in experimental acute spinal cord injury. Journal of clinical neuroscience: *official journal of the Neurosurgical Society of Australasia*, 15(5), 541-544.

[4]   Devivo, M. J. (2012). Epidemiology of traumatic spinal cord injury: trends and future implications. *Spinal cord*, 50(5), 365-372.

[5]   Donato, R. (1986). S-100 proteins. *Cell calcium*, 7(3), 123-145.

[6]   Fassbender, K., Schmidt, R., Schreiner, A., Fatar, M., Muhlhauser, F., et al. (1997). Leakage of brain-originated proteins in peripheral blood: temporal profile and diagnostic value in early ischemic stroke. *Journal of the neurological sciences*, 148(1), 101-105.

[7] Guez, M., Hildingsson, C., Rosengren, L., Karlsson, K. & Toolanen, G. (2003). Nervous tissue damage markers in cerebrospinal fluid after cervical spine injuries and whiplash trauma. *Journal of neurotrauma*, *20*(9), 853-858.

[8] Kang, S. K., So, H. H., Moon, Y. S. & Kim, C. H. (2006). Proteomic analysis of injured spinal cord tissue proteins using 2-DE and MALDI-TOF MS. *Proteomics*, *6*(9), 2797-2812.

[9] Khaladj, N., Teebken, O. E., Hagl, C., Wilhelmi, M. H., Tschan, C., et al. (2008). The role of cerebrospinal fluid S100 and lactate to predict clinically evident spinal cord ischaemia in thoraco-abdominal aortic surgery. European journal of vascular and endovascular surgery: *the official journal of the European Society for Vascular Surgery*, *36*(1), 11-19.

[10] Kunihara, T., Shiiya, N. & Yasuda, K. (2001). Changes in S100beta protein levels in cerebrospinal fluid after thoracoabdominal aortic operations. *The Journal of thoracic and cardiovascular surgery*, *122*(5), 1019-1020.

[11] Kwon, B. K., Casha, S., Hurlbert, R. J. & Yong, V. W. (2011). Inflammatory and structural biomarkers in acute traumatic spinal cord injury. Clinical chemistry and laboratory medicine: *CCLM/FESCC*, *49*(3), 425-433.

[12] Kwon, B. K., Stammers, A. M., Belanger, L. M., Bernardo, A., Chan, D., et al. (2010). Cerebrospinal fluid inflammatory cytokines and biomarkers of injury severity in acute human spinal cord injury. *Journal of neurotrauma*, *27*(4), 669-682.

[13] Lam, T., Noonan, V. K. & Eng, J. J. (2008). A systematic review of functional ambulation outcome measures in spinal cord injury. *Spinal cord*, *46*(4), 246-254.

[14] Loy, D. N., Sroufe, A. E., Pelt, J. L., Burke, D. A., Cao, Q. L., et al. (2005). Serum biomarkers for experimental acute spinal cord injury: rapid elevation of neuron-specific enolase and S-100beta. *Neurosurgery*, *56*(2), 391-397; discussion 391-397.

[15] Lubieniecka, J. M., Streijger, F., Lee, J. H., Stoynov, N., Liu, J., et al. (2011) Biomarkers for severity of spinal cord injury in the cerebrospinal fluid of rats. *PloS one.*, *6*(4), e19247.

[16] Ma, J., Novikov, L. N., Karlsson, K., Kellerth, J. O. & Wiberg, M. (2001). Plexus avulsion and spinal cord injury increase the serum concentration of S-100 protein: an experimental study in rats. *Scandinavian journal of plastic and reconstructive surgery and hand*

surgery/Nordisk plastikkirurgisk forening [and] Nordisk klubb for handkirurgi, 35(4), 355-359.

[17] Marquardt, G., Setzer, M. & Seifert, V. (2004). Protein S-100b as serum marker for prediction of functional outcome in metastatic spinal cord compression. *Acta neurochirurgica, 146*(5), 449-452.

[18] Marquardt, G., Setzer, M. & Seifert, V. (2004). Protein S-100b for individual prediction of functional outcome in spinal epidural empyema. *Spine, 29*(1), 59-62.

[19] Pouw, M. H., Hosman, A. J., van Middendorp, J. J., Verbeek, M. M., Vos, P. E., et al. (2009). Biomarkers in spinal cord injury. *Spinal cord, 47*(7), 519-525.

[20] Skouen, J. S., Brisby, H., Otani, K., Olmarker, K., Rosengren, L., et al. (1999). Protein markers in cerebrospinal fluid in experimental nerve root injury. A study of slow-onset chronic compression effects or the biochemical effects of nucleus pulposus on sacral nerve roots. *Spine, 24*(21), 2195-2200.

[21] Vaccaro, A. R., Klein, G. R., Ciccoti, M., Pfaff, W. L., Moulton, M. J., et al. (2002). Return to play criteria for the athlete with cervical spine injuries resulting in stinger and transient quadriplegia/paresis. *The spine journal: official journal of the North American Spine Society, 2*(5), 351-356.

[22] van Dongen, E. P., Ter Beek, H. T., Boezeman, E. H., Schepens, M. A., Langemeijer, H. J., et al. (1998). Normal serum concentrations of S-100 protein and changes in cerebrospinal fluid concentrations of S-100 protein during and after thoracoabdominal aortic aneurysm surgery: Is S-100 protein a biochemical marker of clinical value in detecting spinal cord ischemia? *Journal of vascular surgery, 27*(2), 344-346.

[23] van Dongen, E. P., ter Beek, H. T., Schepens, M. A., Morshuis, W. J., Haas, F. J., et al. (1999). The relationship between evoked potentials and measurements of S-100 protein in cerebrospinal fluid during and after thoracoabdominal aortic aneurysm surgery. *Journal of vascular surgery, 30*(2), 293-300.

[24] Winnerkvist, A., Anderson, R. E., Hansson, L. O., Rosengren, L., Estrera, A. E., et al. (2007). Multilevel somatosensory evoked potentials and cerebrospinal proteins: indicators of spinal cord injury in thoracoabdominal aortic aneurysm surgery. European journal of cardio-thoracic surgery: *official journal of the European Association for Cardio-thoracic Surgery, 31*(4), 637-642.

In: Cerebrospinal Fluid
Editor: Lawrence E. Keen

ISBN: 978-1-63117-908-2
© 2014 Nova Science Publishers, Inc.

Chapter 2

Cerebrospinal Fluid: Novel Developed Biomarkers in Neurological Disease

M. Dessi, F. Duranti, M. Pieri, G. Sancesario,
R. Zenobi and S. Bernardini
Department of Experimental Medicine and Surgery,
"Tor Vergata" University Hospital, Rome

Abstract

The cerebrospinal fluid (CSF) is a dynamic, metabolically active fluid that occupies the subarachnoid space and the ventricular system around the brain, and has many important functions. CSF is a promising body fluid for the search of biomarkers associated with neurological disease, because CSF has more physical contact with brain than any other fluid, and biochemical changes related to many pathologies may be reflected in the CSF.

Although CSF is obtained by lumbar puncture, invasive and potentially painful for the patient, it is probably the most informative fluid in biomarkers discovery for neurological disease prognosis. Basic CSF diagnostics tests, such as the CSF/serum albumin ratio and CSF cell counts, have been used to diagnose inflammatory and infectious CNS disorders in adults and children for decades. The use of biomarkers is increasingly proposed as a method to refine the diagnosis and guide the treatment of numerous diseases. In this chapter, we review the development of candidate biomarkers in CSF and serum for different pathologies. We focus on established biomarkers, those that have been evaluated in several studies by different research groups, and we discuss their implementation in clinical routines and their potential role in clinical trials.

Besides the state of art about what is known on classical CSF biomarkers for early diagnosis in routine clinical practice, there also are international research initiatives aimed at identifying new biomarkers for detection, and monitoring of pathological processes in the brain. Recently biomarkers are useful in detecting the preclinical as well as the symptomatic stages of Alzheimer Disease (AD). The core CSF biomarkers total tau (T-tau), phosphorylated tau (P-tau) and the 42 amino acid form of b-amyloid (Ab42) reflect AD pathology, and are highly accurate in diagnosing AD with dementia and prodromal AD in mild cognitive impairment cases. Among recognized mediators, other new methods and tests can help highlight inflammatory or neurodegenerative processes in the CNS, accumulating evidence indicates that interleukin-6 (IL-6) is a new potential marker of CNS diseases. Another new test specific to diagnosing multiple sclerosis (MS) is the nephelometric assay for k free light chain determination and kFLC Index calculation in cerebrospinal fluid and serum. Only the CSF oliglonal band and IgG index are currently used to assist with MS diagnosis. The new nephelometric test may be a useful procedure for detection, potentially for monitoring intrathecal immunoglobulin synthesis, and to permit a rapid discriminatory diagnosis of MS.

In this chapter, we discuss the recent advancements of clinical diagnostic CSF tests with particular emphasis on possible new biomarkers for monitoring the early development of CNS disease before significant cognitive dysfunction and also to stratify clinical prognosis.

Finally the rationale for the use of CSF biomarkers to identify and monitor the mechanism of action of new drug candidates is also outlined in this chapter.

Introduction

Cerebrospinal fluid (CSF) is a promising source for the research of biomarkers associated with neurological disorders, because it is a dynamic, metabolically active fluid and it is in direct contact with the brain. The use of biomarkers is emerging as a tool to investigate the underlying mechanisms of pathologies, supporting the diagnosis in vivo and guiding the treatment. In this chapter, we focus on established biomarkers of CSF for the diagnosis and progression of neurological pathologies, with particular emphasis on newly developed biomarkers for the early diagnosis of neurodegenerative and neoplastic diseases, other than commonly used tests for infectious and autoimmune diseases. Moreover, we discuss the main pre-analytical and analytical problems affecting CSF analysis and the progress in biomarker's research.

History

The history of liquor is very ancient; its existence is already described in the Edwin Smith surgical papyrus from about 1500 BC. Several authors over the centuries have helped to improve the knowledge of the anatomy of the central nervous system (CNS) and the physiology of the CSF. The presence of fluid in the brain was known to the ancient physicians Hippocrates (460-375 BC), when describing congenital hydrocephalus and after, from Galen (130-200), the premier anatomist. Despite the recognition by Hippocrates and Galen of some kind of fluid in the brain, subsequent anatomists missed it for 16 centuries, perhaps due to their autopsy technique, i.e., cutting off the head from the neck, which drained the CSF and blood from the brain and spine. The discovery of CSF is attributed to Emanuel Swedenborg (1688-1772), while Francois Magendie (1783-1855) studied the property of CSF by experimenting on living animals and discovered the foramen magendie. Four decades after Magendi's studies, rapid advances occurred in understanding the role of CSF.

In 1891, W. Essex Wynter (1860-1945) treated tuberculous meningitis by tapping the spinal subarachnoidal space. Heinrich Quincke popularized lumbar puncture by presenting the technique at the German Congress of Medicine and advocating its use to examine the constituents of the CSF for diagnostic and therapeutic purposes [1].

For a long time, the essential function of CSF was considered to be that of a fluid envelope that protects the central nervous system. Recent data derived from molecular biology show that CSF plays an essential role in homeostasis of the interstitial fluid of the brain parenchyma and regulation of neuronal functioning.

CSF Anatomy and Physiology

CSF is a clear and colorless liquid that surrounds the brain and the spinal cord providing a mechanical barrier against shock and lubrication between surrounding bones. The CSF is continuously formed almost exclusively by choroid plexuses and a residual from blood ultrafiltration; the total volume varied from 60 to 200 ml. Liquor has a different composition from that of the plasma (Table 1).

Water, oxygen and carbon dioxide easily flow from the blood to CSF mediated passive diffusion through the membranes, while some ions arrive in the CSF with extreme difficulty. CSF has a very low protein constituent, with only albumin being present together with a very low level of cellularity.

Table 1. Cytological and biochemical composition of liquor and serum

Parameters	Liquor	Serum
RBC	None	3,5-5,0 millions
WBC	0-5	4500-11000
Osmolarity	295 mEq/L	295 mEq/L
Na	138 mEq/L	138 mEq/L
k	2.8 mEq/L	4.1 mEq/L
Ca	2.4 mEq/L	5.2 mEq/L
Mg	2.7 mEq/L	1.9 mEq/L
Cl	124 mEq/L	101 mEq/L
P	1.6 mg/dL	4 mg/dL
Bicarbonate	23 mEq/L	23 mEq/L
pH	7.31	7.41
Ammonium	30μg/dL	70μg/dL
Urea	4.7 mmol/L	5.4 mmol/L
Uric acid	0.24 mg/dL	4 mg/dL
Creatinine	1.1 mg/dL	1.6 mg/dL
Lipids	1.25 mg/dL	876 mg/dL
Glucose	>45 mg/dL	90 mg/dL
Lactate	1.6 mEq/L	1 mEq/L
Total proteins	0.015-0.050 g/dL	6.5-8.4 g/dL
Albumin	60%	65%

CSF and blood are separated from blood-brain barrier (BBB), with the task of maintaining the delicate chemical and physical homeostasis. BBB is situated at the level of the choroid plexus of the cerebral ventricles and has both an anatomical (capillary wall cells of the choroid and choroid) and a dynamic-functional nature. It is a set of mechanisms that regulate the passage of substances from the blood to the CNS and protect the latter from any damage by toxic substances (Figure 1).

Transfer speed of substances from the blood to the CSF is directly proportional to their lipid solubility and inversely proportional to their molecular size. Thus, for example, fat-soluble small molecules such as ethyl alcohol spread easily and the same happens for some anesthetics such as thiopental; there are, however, water-soluble substances such as glucose which pass easily into the CSF by the presence of specific transport systems (facilitated diffusion). The proteins slowly move from the blood to the CSF and this explains why they have a concentration of hundreds of times lower in CSF than in plasma (Figure 2). This is important because each time the ratio of $CSF_{albumin}$ and $blood_{albumin}$ increases means that there has been an alteration of the BBB.

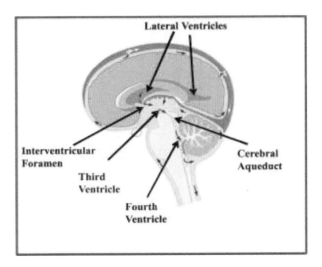

Figure 1. CSF circulation, due to hydrostatic pressure, starts from the choroid plexus of the lateral ventricles and through the interventricular foramina arrives into the 3rd ventricle. CSF then flows through the cerebral aqueduct into the 4th ventricle. From the 4th ventricle the CSF may flow down the central canal of the spinal cord, or circulate in the subarachnoid space. Once in the subarachnoid space, the CSF may enter the cerebromedullary cistern (a dilation of the subarachnoid space between the cerebellum and the medulla) and then circulate over the cerebral hemispheres. CSF also flows down the length of the spinal cord in the subarachnoid space. Arachnoid granulations contain many villi that are able to act as a one-way valve helping to regulate pressure within the CSF, and these arachnoid villi push through the dura and into the venous sinuses.

SERUM

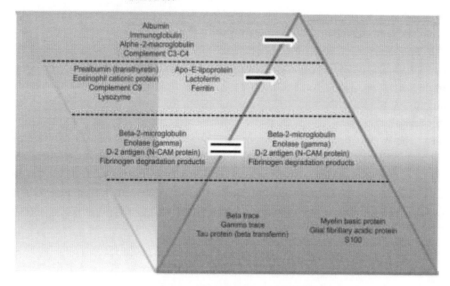

LIQUOR

Figure 2. Protein diffusion at the blood-brain barrier level.

The CSF fulfills several and very important functions:

- Protection function: protects the brain and spinal cord from any trauma or shock against the bony structures that contain it.
- Nutrition function: CSF is the vehicle to distribute the nutrients in the central nervous system exchanging substances between the blood and the brain. It is the transport system for waste products.
- Intra-cranical pressure regulation: this function prevents cerebral ischemia. The CSF, in fact, adapts its volume to variations in blood flow and cerebral mass: in so doing, it keeps both the pressure and the intracranial volume constant.
- Transport function: dispense at CNS neurotransmitters and neuroendocrine substances.

In pathological conditions CSF composition can be altered and its analysis may reflect CNS pathological alterations in the major parts of neurological disease.

CSF Analysis

Sample Collection

The CSF is accessible to trained clinicians using a lumbar puncture (LP) in vertebral body L3–L5, relatively simple and only slightly invasive, which, if it is correctly done, does not provoke headache or other complications [2]. The high diagnostic capacities, which have been recently reported also for prodromal stages of senile dementia, have provided a new interest in the employment of CSF analysis [3, 4]. With particular interest on Alzheimer Disease (AD) biomarkers (beta-amyloid protein fragment 1-42 ($A\beta_{42}$), T-tau and p-tau (181p)), significant variability in concentration and diagnostic performance of the same biomarker across different studies have hampered the application of these molecular tests for general clinical diagnostic purposes. Such discrepancy in the detection of CSF biomarkers could be the result of several pre-analytical and analytical factors, or could be dependent on manufacturing processes that impact assay-related factors [5-7]. Thus, ABSI (Alzheimer's Biomarkers Standardization Initiative) has approved common guidelines for CSF handling and processing [8] in order to reach analytical standardization between laboratories and enable results for the AD biomarkers in CSF to be comparable between different sites, favoring the inclusion of CSF biomarkers in routine analysis [9, 10] and clinical trials [4].

Routine Analysis

Routine analysis performed on CSF includes physical, cytological, chemical, microbiological and molecular analysis that could reveal underlying pathological processes.

Physical Analysis

Opening Pressure

Normal opening pressure (ranges from 10 to 100 mm H_2O in young children, 60 to 200 mm H_2O after eight years of age, and up to 250 mm H_2O in obese patients) can be altered (lower) as an effect of trauma or if the patient has had a previous lumbar puncture, whereas it can increase in pathologic states, including meningitis, intracranial hemorrhage, and tumors.

Aspect and Color

CSF is normally defined as limpid crystal clear, and modification of its aspect can be attributed to infectious and inflammatory conditions that must be discriminated from the traumatic tap. The presence of at least 200 white blood cells (WBCs)/μl or 400 red blood cells (RBCs)/μl will cause CSF to appear turbid, while xanthochromia (the yellow, orange, or pink discoloration of the CSF) after centrifugation is caused by the lysis of RBCs resulting in hemoglobin breakdown to oxyhemoglobin, methemoglobin, and bilirubin. CSF in newborns could appear xanthochromic because of the frequent elevation of bilirubin and protein levels in this age group (Table 2).

Table 2. Cerebrospinal Fluid Supernatant Colors and Associated Conditions or Causes

Color of CSF supernatant	Conditions or causes
Yellow	Blood breakdown products
	Hyperbilirubinemia
	CSF protein ≥150 mg per dL
	>100,000 red blood cells per mmc
Orange	Blood breakdown products
	High carotenoid ingestion
Pink	Blood breakdown products
Green	Hyperbilirubinemia
	Purulent CSF
Brown	Meningeal melanomatosis

Cytological Analysis

Cytological evaluation should be performed within 2 hours after puncture, in order to avoid lysis of both RBC and WBC. Normal CSF contains up to 5 WBC/μl in adults and 20 WBC/μl in newborns that increase in CNS infection, intracerebral hemorrhage, after a seizure, with malignancy and in a variety of inflammatory conditions. Common practice is to measure cell counts in three consecutive tubes of CSF: if the number of RBCs is relatively constant, then it is assumed that the blood in CSF is caused by an intracranial hemorrhage; oppositely, falling count is attributed to a traumatic tap. The evaluation of cellular differentiation, e.g., by May–Grunwald–Giemsa staining, also allows verification of the eventual presence of malignant cells. In normal adult CSF the WBC count is comprised of lymphocytes and monocytes (Table 3).

Table 3. Possible causes in WBC alterations

Findings	Causes
↑ lymphocytes	Meningitis: -viral -fungal -tubercular -parasitic Multiple sclerosis Guillain-Barrè syndrome Toxic encephalopathy
↑ neutrophil	Meningitis: -bacterial -fungal -tubercular (initially) -viral (initially) Cerebral abscess Subarachnoid hemorrhage Metastatic tumor
↑ monocytes	Chronic meningitis Multiple sclerosis
↑ eosinophils	Parasitic infection Drug injection in the subarachnoid space

Biochemical Analysis

Glucose

Glucose is the major source of energy for the nerve tissue. The overcoming of BBB occurs through a system of active transport. The glucose concentration in CSF (glycorrhachia) is directly proportional to the blood concentration and its correct evaluation requires the simultaneous determination of the analyte in CSF and serum with the calculation of the ratio CSF/serum (Q_{glu} = Glu_{CSF}/Glu_{serum}). Qglu < 0.4-0.5 is considered a pathological value. Normal CSF glucose is about two thirds of the serum glucose. Glucose in the CSF of neonates varies much more than in adults, and Qglu is generally higher. CNS infections can cause lowered CSF glucose levels, although these are usually normal in viral infections and up to 50% of patients with bacterial meningitis. Chemical meningitis, inflammatory conditions, subarachnoid hemorrhage, and hypoglycemia also cause hypoglycorrhachia. There is no pathologic process that causes hyperglycorrhachia.

Lactate

The CSF normal lactate value is <2.8–3.5 mmol/l and the level is independent of blood concentration because it does not pass the BBB [11]. The clinical relevance of CSF lactate is similar to that of the CSF/serum glucose ratio, because it is useful in differential diagnosis of inflammatory disease. Decreased CSF/serum glucose ratio or increased CSF lactate indicate bacterial and fungal infections or leptomeningeal metastases. An increased level can be detected earlier than the reduced glucose concentration.

Protein

The BBB is a physical barrier, consisting of different anatomical structures, for the diffusion and filtration of macromolecules from blood to CSF. The integrity of these barriers and CSF bulk flow determine the protein content of the CSF [12, 13]. The albumin, synthesized exclusively in the liver, is completely derived from the plasma and constitutes about 60% of the proteins in cerebrospinal fluid. Measurement of CSF protein concentration is one of the most sensitive indicators of pathology within the CNS. Normal levels range from 0.18 to 0.58 g/L in adult up to 1.5g/L in newborn. However, each laboratory, based on population and specific techniques employed, should define the normal reference range. The relationship between CSF and serum albumin ($Q_{alb}=Alb_{CSF}/Alb_{serum}$) provides information on the integrity of BBB; Q_{alb} follow a concentration gradient along the neuraxis, the lowest concentrations in the ventricular fluid and the highest in the lumbar sac. Elevated CSF protein occurs in infections, intracranial hemorrhages, multiple sclerosis, Guillain Barré syndrome, malignancies, some endocrine abnormalities, certain medication use and a variety of inflammatory conditions. Interestingly, CSF protein levels do not fall in hypoproteinemia. Immunoglobulins (IgG, IgA, IgM) in CSF originate in plasma, but in some diseases can be produced intrathecally, highlighting the immunological activation of the CNS. Recent literature supports increasing evidence that the inflammatory process in the CNS is present in many neurological diseases. The most common parameters used for the evaluation of inflammation in the CNS are:

- increased Q_{Alb}
- increased intrathecal synthesis (IS) Immunoglobulin (Ig) assessed with quantitative methods (index Ig and hyperbolic function, indexes free light chains) or by qualitative analysis that demonstrates the presence of oligoclonal bands (OBCs).

Intrathecal synthesis refers to any condition involving synthesis of a specific protein in the CNS; but only the synthesis of IgG currently plays an important diagnostic role in neurological diseases. Oligoclonal bands are discrete bands in the gamma region of the CSF electrophoretic pattern that were not present in the serum pattern.

Beta-Trace Protein

Beta-trace protein constitutes about 7% of the total CSF protein concentration, the concentration of beta-trace protein was found to increase with age. The major site of biosynthesis are the leptomeninges and to some extent the choroid plexus. Beta-trace protein is the best routine method to detect a CSF rhinorrhea and CSF otorrhea [14].

Microbiological Analysis

Laboratory examination of the CSF is usually the first step to confirm the presence of infectious meningitis. Note that cytological examination should precede centrifugation and heating of the CSF.

Microscopic Examination

The Gram stain is a method for differentiating bacterial species into two large groups based on the chemical and physical properties of their cell walls. Gram-positive bacteria (dark violet or purple) retain the primary stain while gram-negative (red or pink) bacteria take the color of the counterstain.

Gram stain is positive in 60 to 80% of untreated cases of bacterial meningitis and in 40 to 60% of partially treated cases. The sensitivity, according to the causative organism, ranges from 90% in pneumococcal or staphylococcal meningitis to less than 50% in Listeria meningitis; hyphae can occasionally be seen in Candida or other fungal meningitis cases.

Culture

Cultures done on 5% sheep blood agar and enriched chocolate agar remain the gold standards for diagnosing bacterial meningitis [15]. Antibiotic treatment prior to lumbar puncture can decrease the sensitivity of culture, especially when given intravenously or intramuscularly [16]. Enterovirus, the leading cause of viral meningitis, can be recovered in 40 to 80% of cases; culture for herpes simplex virus is 80 to 90% sensitive but can require five to seven days to become positive [17].

Mycobacterium tuberculosis needs a large volume of CSF samples for optimal growth and the culture is positive half of the time on the first sample, and improves to 83% of the time if four separate samples are added, often taking up to six weeks for positive identification [18]. Fungal cultures are positive in more than 95% of Cryptococcus Neoformans cases and in 66% of candidal meningitis cases; other fungi are less likely to be culture positive.

Latex Agglutination

Latex agglutination (LA) allows rapid detection of bacterial antigens in CSF. Several commercial kits are available for LA testing for the detection of soluble bacterial antigens (capsular polysaccharide). Sensitivity varies greatly between bacteria, being very high for Hemophilus influenza (60-100%), but is much lower for other bacteria. LA can be useful in partially treated meningitis cases, where cultures may not detect the presence of organisms. LA is recommended for use in cases of suspected bacterial meningitis if the initial Gram stain and bacterial culture are negative after 48 hours (Figure 3).

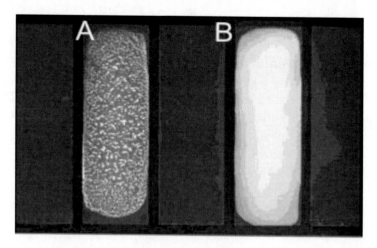

Figure 3. Latex agglutination results. Positive reaction shows agglutination (or visible clumping; A) of the latex particles and slight clearing of the suspension occurs within 2-10 minutes; in negative reaction the suspension remains homogenous and slightly milky in appearance (B).

Flow Cytometry

Recently, flow cytometry with a dedicated bacterial channel was shown to have a possible application in automated cell counting and this novel approach in the differential diagnosis of CNS infection has been explored [19].

Molecular Analysis

Rapid Diagnostic Tests

Rapid diagnostic tests (RDTs) have been developed for direct testing of CSF specimens without prior heat or centrifugation [20]. The test is based on the principle of vertical flow immunochromatography in which gold particles and nitrocellulose membranes are coated with monoclonal antibodies to capture soluble serogroup-specific polysaccharide antigens in the CSF. The test consists of 2 duplex paper sticks (also called dipsticks), which together enable identification of four serogroups of N. meningitides (A, C, W135, and Y).

RDT commercial kits are also available for S. Pneumonia detection by immunochromatography.

Polymerase Chain Reaction

Polymerase chain reaction (PCR) improves the diagnosis of meningitis with high sensitivity and specificity using only small volumes of CSF. In viral meningitis, as herpes simplex virus type 1, Epstein-Barr virus, and enterovirus, the sensitivity ranges from 95 to 100% and specificity reaches the 100% [21]; when PCR is positive for enterovirus, it allows earlier hospital discharge and less intervention [22]. PCR is the most sensitive means of diagnosing Cytomegalovirus (CMV) infections of the CNS and it has been suggested that PCR should replace brain biopsy as the gold standard for herpes encephalitis [23]. PCR has a sensitivity of 54 to 100% and a specificity of 94 to 100% for tuberculous meningitis, and could replace acid-fast bacillus smear and culture as the test of choice [24]. PCR is sensitive for acute neurosyphilis but not for more chronic forms. PCR also is being studied as a diagnostic tool for bacterial meningitis and other infections of the CNS.

Infectious Disease

Meningitis

Most cases of meningitis are due to a bacterial or viral infection. Viral or aseptic meningitis are most frequently caused by an enterovirus and usually resolve without treatment (self-limited). Less common causes include: Herpes simplex virus (HSV), Epstein-Barr virus, Influenza, Mumps, Measles, Varicella-zoster virus (VZV), Arboviruses.

Bacterial meningitis is generally considered a medical emergency; rapid identification and treatment are crucial because untreated bacterial meningitis is usually fatal. The most common causes are: N. Meningitides, S. pneumonia and H. Influenza.

Fungal meningitis, though rare, is not contagious and is commonly seen in immune-compromised patients, such as those with HIV, and is mainly due to Cryptococcus neoformans; other causes include Coccidioides, Histoplasma and Candida species. Parasitic meningitis is rare and can be lethal.

Chronic meningitis is infection that lasts for more than four weeks and may be caused by bacteria such as Mycobacterium tuberculosis, Treponema pallidum and fungi.

The majority of patients (87%) with bacterial meningitis have a WBC count higher than 1,000/mmc, while the 12% have more than 100 WBCs/mmc. In viral meningitis, WBCs are commonly less than 100/mmc.

The cell differential alone cannot distinguish between bacterial and non-bacterial meningitis. Lymphocytosis is seen in viral, fungal, and tuberculous infections of the CNS, although a predominance of polymorphonuclear cells (PMNs) may be present in the early stages of these infections. CSF in bacterial meningitis is typically dominated by the presence of PMNs, however, more than 10% of bacterial meningitis cases will show a lymphocytic predominance, especially early in the clinical course and when there are fewer than 1,000 WBCs/mmc (Table 4).

Eosinophilic meningitis is defined as more than 10 eosinophils/mmc or a total CSF cell count reveals more than 10% eosinophils. Parasitic infection should be suspected in this situation, but other possible causes may include viral, fungal, or rickettsial meningitis, ventriculoperitoneal shunts with or without coexisting infection, malignancy and adverse drug reactions [25].

**Table 4. Typical Cerebrospinal Fluid Findings in
Various Types of Meningitis**

Test	Bacterial	Viral	Fungal	Tubercular
Opening pressure	Elevated	Usually normal	Variable	Variable
WBC count	≥1,000 per mmc	<100 per mmc	Variable	Variable
Cell differential	Predominance of PMNs	Predominance of lymphocytes	Predominance of lymphocytes	Predominance of lymphocytes
Protein	Mild to marked elevation	Normal to elevated	Elevated	Elevated
CSF/serum glucose	Normal to marked decrease	Usually normal	Low	Low

Encephalitis

Encephalitis is an acute infection of the brain characterized by fever, headache, and an altered state of consciousness, with or without seizures. Most cases of encephalitis are caused by viruses including: Herpes simplex virus (HSV), Enteroviruses, the rabies virus (from an animal bite) and Arboviruses. CSF profile is similar to that showed in the cases of viral meningitis, with PCR as a sensible and rapid assay. Bacterial, fungal and parasitic encephalitis are very rare. Bacterial meningoencephalitis may develop from the bacteria that causes meningitis.

Tick transmitted Lyme disease may cause bacterial meningoencephalitis: CSF Borrelia Burgdorferi IgM and/or IgG antibodies may also be aspecifically positive in infections caused by other bacteria, such as the Treponema Pallidum. Borrelia Burgdorferi Western Blot is necessary to confirm positive or indeterminate antibody test results. PCRtesting is occasionally performed on CSF to detect Borrelia Burgdorferi genetic material.

Brain Abscess

Brain abscess (BA) is the only CNS infection in which LP is never recommended and may even be contraindicated. In the Nathoo et al. series [26], pretransfer LP had been performed in 193 patients (19.8%) before consultation, which was followed by neurological deterioration in 26 patients (13.5%), with 7 deaths. CSF analysis revealed nonspecific pleocytosis with increased protein and no organism cultured in 80 patients (41.5%), bacterial meningitis in 71 patients (36.8%), and was normal in 31 patients. No data were available in 11 patients. This advice is not only because an LP does not help in the diagnosis but also because increased intracranial pressure (ICP) is often present as a result of the mass effect, which increases the likelihood of herniation, complicating clinical status of the patient.

Autoimmune Disease

Guillain-Barré Syndrome

Guillain-Barré syndrome (GBS) is an acute inflammatory demyelinating polyneuropathy (AIDP), an autoimmune disease affecting the peripheral nervous system that is usually triggered by an acute infectious process. Its relation to infection and its status as an autoimmune disease have stimulated much research over the years, which have resulted in the discovery of antiganglioside antibodies in at least one third of GBS patients. These antibodies appear to cross-react with antigens in the lipopolysaccharides of some antecedent infective agents, providing a possible mechanism for the disease. In addition to nerve conduction studies (NCS) and electromyography (EMG), CSF analysis may confirm a diagnosis of GBS. A raised CSF protein concentration is present in 80% of patients, with the mononuclear cell count being either normal (albuminocytologic dissociation) or < 50 cells/mmc [27]. The CSF is normal in the first week of the illness.

Autoimmune Encephalopathies

The field of autoimmune encephalopathies has expanded rapidly in the last few years [28]. It is now well-established that a substantial proportion of encephalitides are associated with autoantibodies directed against the extracellular domains of cell-surface proteins which are critical in the regulation of neuronal excitability. These include LGI1[29], CASPR2 [30], contactin-2 (VGKC-complex antibodies) [31], and the NMDA [32], AMPA [33], and GABAB [34] receptors. The clinical importance of these conditions lies in their frequent immunotherapy-response and, less commonly, their association with distinctive tumors. The generation of the autoantibody, in some patients, can be explained by the presence of tumors, which express their antigenic target. However, the majority of patients do not harbor a tumor and the etiology of the disease in these patients is less clear. As all these antibodies are serum-predominant in the majority of cases, but have their effect within the CNS, if serum or CSF antibody reductions, which best correlate with clinical outcome, is an unanswered question at the current state of art. The latter may be answered with serial studies of antibodies in both serum and CSF, in conjunction with quantitative methods to assess clinical recovery.

Neoplastic Disease

Primary CNS Tumors

CSF analysis in primary CNS tumors is not indicated because diagnosis is based on clinical symptoms and radiological imaging, but may be useful if, after initial investigations, the nature of the lesion has not yet been clarified. LP is contraindicated if there is papilledema or if other symptoms or signs indicate increased intracranial pressure and should not be practiced until the CT scan or magnetic resonance imaging (MRI) have ruled out lesions with mass effect, otherwise the sudden change in CSF pressure may cause a cerebral herniation. Actually CSF biomarkers for detecting primary CNS tumors are not still validated.

Neoplastic Meningitis

Neoplastic meningitis (NM) results from the spread of malignant cells to the leptomeninges and subarachnoid space and their dissemination within the CSF compartment. NM is a frequent complication of systemic cancer and occurs in 4%–15% of all patients with solid tumors. Although NM has been described in nearly all types of solid tumors, the most common solid tumors causing NM are breast cancer (43%), lung cancer (31%), and melanoma (6%) [35, 36]. In the last few years, it was discovered that the molecular factors implicated in NM development are numerous, including, in particular, metalloproteinases, activated integrin, vascular endothelial growth factor (VEGF), and epidermal growth factor receptor (EGFR)-2 protein [37]. The diagnosis of NM is based on clinical symptoms and signs, imaging evidence, and CSF analysis.

CSF analysis could represent a valid method for diagnosis because the demonstration of tumor cells in the CSF is diagnostic for NM and anyone suspected of having NM should have a LP performed, if it is not otherwise contraindicated. CSF cytology is tumor positive on the first LP in 50% of cases [38], increasing to about 90% with a second LP, but little benefit is obtained from additional LPs [39]. However, CSF cytology can remain falsely negative in 14% of patients even after three samples.

MRI and CSF cytology can be complementary for the NM diagnosis. When cytology is not diagnostic, measurement of the CSF opening pressure, cell count, protein and glucose can be helpful for the diagnosis, although these parameters are very nonspecific; a completely normal routine CSF examination almost excludes NM, and an opening pressure 15 cm H_2O, elevated WBC, glucose 60 mg/dL, or protein 50 mg/dL can be suggestive of NM. In an effort to improve the sensitivity of CSF diagnostic immunocytochemistry, flow cytometry, polymerase chain reaction (PCR), and cytogenetic analysis were developed, although results have been less successful. In addition, numerous nonspecific markers, such as lactate dehydrogenase, or specific markers, such as alfa-fetoprotein or CEA [40], may be useful for monitoring the course of disease; in particular, VEGF was shown to be a sensitive and specific marker for diagnosis and prognosis [41, 42]. Recently, it was shown that Dickkopf related protein 3, a secreted tumor suppressor, may be a useful biologic marker for both the diagnosis and treatment response evaluation of NM, although its specificity is limited by similar CSF levels in patients with viral meningitis [43].

Hematological Malignancies

In patients with NM, early diagnosis is highly desirable because the rapid institution of intrathecal therapy may mitigate the course of the disease. Cytology, long considered the "gold standard" for diagnosis, has low sensitivity because of both the paucity of cells in CSF [44] and morphological similarities between benign and malignant cells [45]. A comprehensive review of the literature from 2005 through 2011 was performed that focused on diagnostic modalities for lymphomatous meningitis. Several studies demonstrated the sensitivity of flow cytometry to be several-fold higher than that of cytology for the detection of CSF leukemia/lymphoma.

Patients with negative cytology but positive flow cytometry results are often asymptomatic and have lower CSF cell counts and neoplastic B-cells compared with patients with positive cytology findings. In patients with aggressive non-Hodgkin's lymphoma (NHL) and risk factors for CNS recurrence, careful monitoring for CNS disease is imperative. The specificity of both cytology and flow cytometry approaches 100%; false positive findings are rare. Flow cytometry is a highly sensitive technique capable of accurately detecting malignant cells, even in samples with very low cell counts. Flow cytometry allows for the earlier detection of NM before the onset of clinical symptoms and CSF pleocytosis and therefore may enable more effective treatment. Future consensus regarding standardized flow cytometric antibody panels, with uniform definitions of positivity, is likely to further advance the early detection of NM by flow cytometry and permit broader clinical applicability. To the best of our knowledge, no consensus exists regarding the optimal antibody selection and combination, but previous histologic diagnosis and the patient's clinical history help guide the selection of antibodies.

Standard flow cytometry protocols with accepted antibody panels and uniform definitions of positivity are needed to advance the state of the art.

Future directions in the diagnosis of leptomeningeal lymphoma may include techniques such as microRNA assays.

Subarachnoid Hemorrhage

Subarachnoid hemorrhage (SAH) accounts for 6% of total strokes. Persons with suspected SAH and a normal computed tomography (CT) scan should undergo an LP. RBCs can be found in a SAH and a traumatic tap. Distinguishing between these two entities requires recognition that only within the human body do RBCs break down into bilirubin, otherwise in CSF collected from a traumatic tap it will break down into oxyhemoglobin, but not into bilirubin. Because the breakdown of RBCs can take up to 12 hours, guidelines recommend that the LP should wait until 12 hours after the initial onset of symptoms. Bilirubin will turn fluid yellow (xanthochromia), but visual inspection alone is not considered sufficiently reliable. Xanthochromia is present in more than 90% of patients within 12 hours of SAH onset and in patients with serum bilirubin levels between 10 to 15 mg/dL (171 to 256.5 µmol/L). Therefore, all specimens should undergo spectrophotometry analysis to detect bilirubin [46], which can be detected as long as two weeks after the initial onset of symptoms.

Neurodegenerative Diseases

Neurodegenerative diseases are a group of heterogeneous disorders characterized by irreversible and diffuse neuronal death in selected areas of the CNS, often associated with reactive gliosis, and sometimes evolving in different forms of dementia. Atypical signs and overlapping symptoms challenge the diagnosis in vivo and neuropathological investigations that reveal the presence of amyloid, tau and synuclein aggregates cannot be done in a living patient (except in very limited cases by brain biopsy). Nevertheless, if the brain is practically inaccessible *in vivo*, CSF is easily and safely accessible, and sequestration of insoluble substances and fibrils formation in brain tissue prevents their detection in the CSF.

To date, several biomarkers have been investigated [47] but only some of them, as CSF $A\beta_{42}$, T-tau and p-tau protein, 14-3-3, OBCs, kappa free light chain Index (kFLCs Index) [48] and serum progranulin have almost been included into routine clinical practice for diagnosis of mild cognitive impairment (MCI), AD [4, 49-51], Lewy body dementia (LBD), Creutzfeldt-Jakob disease (CJD) [52], Multiple Sclerosis (MS) and Frontotemporal Dementia (FTD) [53]; some others, such as α-synuclein and Neuro-Filament protein, are emerging as candidate markers for synucleinopathy and axonopathy.

Alzheimer's and Prodromal Alzheimer's Disease

AD is the most common form of dementia in older people and is characterized by extracellular deposit of both monomeric and aggregated Amyloid β (Aβ), mainly $A\beta_{42}$, and intracellular accumulation of tau (T-tau) and hyperphosphorylated tau (P-tau) in senile or neuritic plaques and neurofibrillary tangle [54]. Although both these modifications occur in the brain of AD and constitute the histopathological hallmarks of the disease, it is not known which relationship exists between the two processes and if they are correlated. Such pathological alteration begin 20-30 years before the clinical onset [55] and, interestingly, they are clearly reflected in CSF by the specific reduction of $A\beta_{42}$ and an increase of T-tau and p-tau, even anticipating the manifestation of clinical symptoms. In this view, biomarkers of dementia could be promising predictors of cognitive decline also in non-demented older adults [56] and of progression from MCI to AD [57, 58], although they constitute in essence an epiphenomenon of the disease. Indeed, according to the new research criteria, the diagnosis of AD is made with a very high level of specificity and predictive validity [59] by the presence of both clinical anmestic or nonamnestic impairment and biological evidence, based on CSF analysis [60], structural MRI [61], or molecular neuroimaging with PET [62], which indicate the pathophysiology or the topography of Alzheimer's pathology [50, 63].

Aβ is mainly produced in the brain and then diffuses into the CSF and plasma. $A\beta_{40}$ is the most abundant species, whereas $A\beta_{42}$ has emerged as a useful diagnostic biomarker because of its role in the pathogenic amyloid cascade, by which $A\beta_{42}$ aggregates in fibrils and deposits in senile and neuritic plaques, preventing its transit from the brain into the CSF [64]. Therefore, CSF measurement of both monomeric and aggregated $A\beta_{42}$ has revealed a good diagnostic biomarker in vivo of clinical and pathogenic interest because their concentration is significantly reduced in subjects with AD respect to age-matched controls [65-69]. Interestingly, $A\beta_{42}$ discriminates AD from control with 78% sensibility and 81% specificity, but the accuracy is lower in comparison with other neurological disorders (71% and 63% respectively) and non-AD dementia (65% and 59% respectively) [70]. $A\beta_{42}$ gives an added diagnostic value in such unclear clinical cases in which the clinical diagnostic work–up is not able to discriminate between different form of dementias, as it has been confirmed in autopsy-confirmed AD and non-AD cases [71].

Tau is a microtubule associated protein (MAPT) and is involved in intracellular transport and cytoskeleton stability of the neuronal axons. The level of CSF Tau increases due to neuronal cell death, which is a common feature of neurodegenerative disease, and can be easily detected in CSF representing an important index of degeneration. Tau is normally post-translational modified by the phosphorylation of numerous serine and threonine residues, but abnormal phosphorylation is a key mechanism in Alzheimer's pathology that provokes the production of hyperphosphorylated tau [72], the principal component of the paired helical filaments and the intracellular neurofibrillary tangles (NFTs) [54]. Notwithstanding such prominent role gained by biomarkers in the diagnosis of AD, the lack of established cut-off level for dementia biomarkers in CSF renders the identification of possible AD patients variable, dependent on specific cut-off levels applied in the different centers [10]. P-tau level is significantly increased in AD with respect to controls subjects and patients with other dementia, and a cut-off point of 61 pg/ml p-tau accurately discriminate AD from LBD, with higher accuracy than other biomarkers alone [73, 74]. The

AD CSF profile is defined by the concomitant reduction of $A\beta_{42}$ ($\leq$450 pg/ml) and increase of both t-tau ($\geq$350 pg/ml) and p-tau ($\geq$62pg/ml). In order to reach the best diagnostic performance, the three biomarkers have so far combined together [3]. Ratios of T-tau/ $A\beta_{1-42}$ and P-tau/ $A\beta_{1-42}$ predict future cognitive decline or dementia in still cognitively normal individuals [56]; the INNOTEST amyloid-tau index (IATI), calculated as $A\beta_{1-42}$ concentration / (240 + (1.18 x T-tau concentration), in combination with p-tau >61 pg/ml, allows differential diagnosis between AD and normal aging or other neurological disorders yielding 86% specificity and 85% sensitivity [70]. Importantly, such indexes have to be validated in clinical trial and for the purpose of differential diagnosis of dementia.

Frontotemporal Dementia

The Frontotemporal Dementia (FTD) is a complex heterogeneous group of syndromes characterized by cognitive impairment that can have predominant behavioral and social disorder [75] or primary language disturbances [76]. The degeneration is provoked by the intracellular accumulation of different abnormally-modified proteins: the microtubule-binding protein tau, the transactive response DNA binding protein-43 (TDP-43), the fused-in-sarcoma protein (FUS), while some FTD forms show tau- and TDP-43-negative ubiquitinated inclusions or no significant neuropathological inclusions [77]. Some familiar forms are associated with mutations in the genes of progranulin (GRN) [78, 79], tau (MAPT) [80], and C9orf72 (C9orf72) [81, 82]. Notwithstanding the diversity of the protein involved, the clinical signs of FTD seem to be not directly linked to singular distinctive histopathological features, and also the known genetic mutations, that are exclusively associated with specific underlying neuropathologies, show various clinical manifestations. Moreover, clinical overlap with other dementias and co-existing pathologies complicate the definition of a diagnosis and render the use of biomarkers a requisite for a diagnosis in vivo, to predict the underlying neuropathology and to assign patients their eventual appropriate protein-targeted therapy.

The level of the classical biomarkers of dementia, T-tau and $A\beta_{42}$, are normal in CSF of FTD patients [83] and can be useful by excluding an AD type dementia.

Progranulin (PGRN), or epithelin precursor, is a cysteine-rich secreted grown factor with neurotrophic properties [84]. Heterozygous mutations in the granulin (GRN) gene is implicated in up to 25% cases of FTD, inherited in autosomal dominant fashion with high penetrance [85]. The measurement of PGRN can easily identify carriers of GRN mutations by the decrease in level of PGRN both in blood and CSF. Therefore, low CSF or less invasive serum PGRN is a specific marker for patients and asymptomatic carriers of GRN mutations, while normal levels of PGRN cannot discriminate other causes of FTD from controls [86, 87]. FUS levels have not been fully explored nor has any marker been identified for C9ORF72 mutation.

Vascular Dementia

Vascular dementia (VaD) is a cognitive disorder caused by presumed vascular damage in any brain territory that can produce a continuum of abnormalities depending on the site and spread of the damage. Therefore, the clinical, neuroimaging and pathologic phenotypes of the vascular injury may be heterogeneous, and the co-existence with other pathologies, in particular AD, that determines a mixed-dementia (MD) complicating the definition of the differential diagnosis [88-91]. Moreover, a vascular cognitive impairment (VCI) can also occur in the absence of dementia [92-94].

Once again, $A\beta_{42}$, T-tau and p-tau can help the discrimination of "pure" VaD from VCI, AD and MD [95]. In fact, the typical AD profile (low levels of $A\beta_{42}$, and high T-tau and P-tau) is not modified in presence of vascular damage and can discriminate AD from VCI that shows $A\beta_{42}$ and p-tau levels similar to control and significant increase of T-tau alone [96]. Normal $A\beta_{42}$ seems to be a predictive factor for identifying VaD with respect to AD and to AD with a secondary vascular event. Finally, in MD the CSF $A\beta_{42}$ is decreased and T-tau increased. Nevertheless, the possible co-occurrence of neuropathological changes associated with age and AD in VCI that can interfere with the correct diagnosis [97] hampering the definition of normative CSF biomarkers levels: T-tau can be increased [96, 98-100], normal [101-103], or intermediate [102, 104], but in any case much lower than in AD; $A\beta_{42}$ can be moderately decreased [96] or significantly overlapping with AD [105]; p-tau can be normal [106] or increased [107]. The best performance for accurate classification of 85-89% cases with VCI, AD and MD can be achieved by the combination of all the three biomarkers together [102].

Parkinson's Disease

Parkinson disease is the second most common form of neurodegenerative disease, after AD that affects aging population over 65. Degeneration involves regions in the CNS that affect motor pathways, producing tremor, slowed movements, rigidity and postural instability, and more than others affects mood, motivation and other functions. The pathological hallmark is the abnormal accumulation of intracellular aggregates composed mainly of abnormal α-synuclein (αSyn) in the cell body, the so called Lewy bodies [108-110], and in the presynaptic terminals [111, 112], that constitutes the key feature of synucleinopathy. As observed in the prodromal phase of AD, pathological modifications begin years before the clinical onset, thus encouraging the research of biomarkers for early and accurate diagnosis. The CSF αSyn together with T-tau, p-tau and $A\beta_{42}$ have been considered promising biomarkers because of their correlation with biologic pathological modifications.

The αSyn is a cytoplasmatic protein, mainly localized in the presynaptic neuronal terminals where it is involved in the modulation of neurotransmitters release [113-117]. It has been hypothesized that a reduction of αSyn concentrations in CSF might be due to the intraneuronal accumulation and deposition of aggregated αSyn in Lewy bodies [118]; oppositely, a marked rise in CSF αSyn, as in prion disease, probably results from rapid cell death [119]. The measurement of αSyn in CSF has been described by several groups with controversial results: levels could be lower in patients with PD, LBD and multiple system atrophy (MSA) than in patients without synucleinopathy, e.g., AD [119-123], or overlaps with control and non-demented patients, showing no discriminative ability [124-128]. PD, MSA and LBD have lower CSF αSyn than patients with AD and other neurological disorders [121]. Such discrepancy probably could depend on the presence of pre-analytical confounding factors (sample processing, blood contamination, heterogeneity in control group, concomitant pathologies, etc.).

Numerous genetic, pathologic and biochemical evidence supports a role for tau in the pathogenesis of PD. Accumulation of the phosphorylated tau protein has been observed postmortem in the PD brain and mutation in the *MAPT* gene, which encodes tau, and correlates with increased risk of sporadic PD [129]. So, it has been hypothesized that neurodegeneration can be driven by interaction of misfolded proteins, and synergies between $A\beta_{42}$, tau and αSyn can accelerate neurodegeneration and cognitive decline [130]. In this view, the combination of age, CSF αSyn and T-tau have been proposed to increase the diagnostic accuracy for synucleinopathies [121], while the ratio αSyn /T-tau could discriminate the group of PD from other neurodegenerative disorders, including LBD, AD and FTD [131]. Moreover, reduction of CSF $A\beta_{42}$ clearly discriminates Parkinson with dementia (PDD) from controls and PD without dementia [132] and might represent a predictive marker for rapid cognitive decline in PD patient at baseline [132].

Lewy body dementia

Lewy body dementia (LBD) belongs to the group of synucleinopathies and, together with AD and PD, is one of the most common causes of dementia in the elderly. Diagnosis in vivo is difficult in clinical settings because of overlapping symptoms with other neurological disorders such as AD and PD, but it is crucial for planning the treatment strategies. P-tau yields the higher accuracy as a single variable biomarker for discriminate LBD from AD [73]. The level of αSyn is lower in LBD than in AD and other neurological disorders and intermediate in LBD compared with AD and PD [121]. LBD can be differentiated from PD by the ratio αSyn /T-tau [131].

Creutzfeldt-Jakob Disease

Creutzfeldt-Jakob disease (CJD) is a fatal transmissible spongiform encephalopathy belonging to the group of progressive neurodegenerative conditions caused by prion proteins that undergo conformational changes, with very rapid clinical evolution and short illness duration. Diagnosis can only be confirmed by the post mortem histopathologic examination, but biochemical analysis of the presence of CSF 14-3-3 and tau >1.400 pg/ml [133] represent the best test for in vivo identification of CJD and differentiate from AD and other rapidly progressive dementia. CSF tests are included in the diagnostic criteria by the World Health Organization WHO [134].

Multiple Sclerosis

Multiple sclerosis (MS) is a heterogeneous autoimmune disease that is characterized by inflammation, demyelination, and axonal degeneration in the

CNS. The pathology results from a primary defect in the immune system that affects the components of the myelin sheath, with secondary effects on neuronal cells. CSF oligoclonal IgG bands, IgG index, and the recently developed "kFLC index", based on measurement of the kappa free light chain in CSF and serum [135-139], have proven their diagnostic utility as an indicator of intrathecal immunoglobulin synthesis and of MS pathogenesis, but there is a lack of biomarkers for monitoring or predicting disease progression, irreversible axonal loss and cognitive impairment [140, 141]. Interestingly, reduction of CSF $A\beta_{42}$ is correlated with abnormal cognitive performances and cortical plasticity reduction in MS subjects [142]. Then, although with different pathogenic mechanisms, $A\beta_{42}$ is involved in cognitive dysfunction also in MS. The following parameters have been evaluated as an index of inflammation in the CSF: interleukin (IL)-1b, TNFa and IL-6.

Amyotrophic Lateral Sclerosis

Amyotrophic Lateral Sclerosis (ALS) is a fatal progressive neurodegenerative disease [143], that affects motor neurons in the brainstem, spinal cord, and the motor cortex. Clinical features consist of fasciculation, muscle atrophy and weakness, increased spasticity and hyperreflexia and in the late phase, and respiratory complications that can cause death. The exact pathophysiological mechanisms underlying neurodegeneration remains uncertain; cytoplasmic inclusions of ubiquitin in degenerating neurons have been observed, along with altered excitability, mitochondrial dysfunction, neurofilament accumulation, glial cell activation, glutamate excitotoxicity, oxidative stress, and impairment of the BBB, followed by a strong inflammatory reaction [144, 145].

Nowadays, ALS diagnosis is based on the detection of upper and lower motor neuron signs in the limb and/or bulbar signs, with a history of symptoms progression; imaging studies and electromyography are used to support the clinical diagnosis. CSF biomarkers may give insight into ALS pathophysiology and may be useful for early diagnosis and the development of new therapeutic strategies.

The glutathione peroxidase activity, the hydrogen peroxide concentration, oxygen species (ROS) are increased in the CSF of ALS patients, reflecting diffuse oxidative stress [146-148]; also increased concentration of inflammatory mediators in CSF such as COX-2, and pro-inflammatory cytokines such as IL- 1b, TNF- a and IL -6 have been reported [144].

Astrocytes and microglia help the motor neuron by releasing neurotrophic factors in the CSF (epithelium-derived factor, PEDF; vascular endothelial growth factor, VEGF; and Progranulin, PGRN), which prevent cells from initiating programmed cell death [149, 150].

Another biomarker that we can find in the ALS CSF is p-Tau, its concentration is increased in the early clinical phase and in the later stages seems to stabilize [139]. As regards the $A\beta_{42}$ in ALS, it is accumulated in anterior horn motor neurons and in the final stage of the disease is decreased in the CSF [151].

Glutamate concentrations are elevated in the CSF of 40% of ALS patients, supporting the hypothesis of excitotoxicity [152], moreover, low concentrations of TDP-43 reflects its own accumulation in cortical and spinal neurons [153].

Anyway, due to the heterogeneity of ALS a multiple biomarker panel may be required to differentiate ALS from other neurodegenerative diseases.

Table 5. CSF Biomarkers in neurodegenerative dementia

	Amyloid β_{1-42}	Total Tau	Phospho Tau $_{181}$	Additional Markers	References	
Control Healthy	≥ 450	≤ 350	≤ 62	IATI > 1	[70]	IATI > 1 p-tau>61 pg/ml
Alzheimer's Disease (AD)	≤ 450	≥ 350	≥ 62	IATI < 1	[70]; [50], [59]; [10]; [66]; [67]; [68]; [154]; [155].	-IATI<1 plus p-Tau>61 pg/ml define AD and those MCI who will progress to AD.
Prodromal Alzheimer Disease (asymptomatic AD)	↓	↑	↑	T-tau/Aβ_{42} Ratio	[56]; [156]; [50]	
MCI – developing AD	↓	↑	↑	IATI < 1 T-tau/Aβ_{42} Ratio	[157]; [60]; [58]; [57]; [158]	
MCI non developing AD but other Dementia	↑	↓	↓		[159]	
MCI stable	↑	↓	↓		[159]	
Fronto Temporal Dementia (FTD)	↑	↓	↓	T-tau/Aβ_{42} Ratio	[83]; [160]; [161]; [162]; [163]	A$\beta_{42,}$ T-tau, p-tau and tau/ Aβ_{42} ratio discriminate FTD vs. AD No difference FTD vs Control

Table 5. (Continued)

	Amyloid β_{1-42}	Total Tau	Phospho Tau $_{181}$	Additional Markers	References	
				Progranulin (PGRN)	[53]; [86]; [87]	Low serum PGRN identify asymptomatic and familial FTD caused by GRN gene mutation
Mixed FTD + AD	↓	↑	↑	TDP-43	[164]; [165]	Low $A\beta_{42}$ and high T-tau discriminate Mixed FTD-AD from "pure" FTD
Vascular Dementia (VaD)	↑	↑	↓		[95]; [104];[105]; [96];[102]	Normal $A\beta_{42}$ discriminate VaD vs. AD and Mixed VaD+AD. Increased T-Tau discriminates VaD with VCI vs. control $A\beta_{42}$ and p-tau similar to control and increase of T-tau alone discriminate VCI from AD
Mixed Vascular Dementia + AD	↓	↑	↑			
Vascular Cognitive Impairment	↑	↑	↓			
Parkinson's Disease (PD)	↑	↑	↓	Synuclein (α-syn) <1.6 pg/ µl	[121]	
				Ratio α-syn/Tau	[131]	ratio α-syn/Tau discriminate PD from other neurodegenerative disorders (including DLB, AD and FTD)[131]
Parkinson with Dementia (PDD)	↓	↑	↓		[132]	Low $A\beta_{42}$ discriminate PDD vs. controls and PD without dementia. Low $A\beta_{42}$ predictive of cognitive decline in PD.

	Amyloid β_{1-42}	Total Tau	Phospho Tau $_{181}$	Additional Markers	References	
Lewy Body Dementia (LBD)	↓	↑	↓	↓ α-syn	[166]; [73]; [121]	P-Tau< 61 pg/ml discriminates LBD from AD
Creutzfeldt-Jakob Disease (CJD)	↑	↑↑ > 1400 pg/ml	↓	CSF 14-3-3	[167]; [168]	High T-Tau > 1200pg/ml differentiates CJD from AD and healthy controls
Multiple Sclerosis (MS)	↑	↓	n.d.	Oligoclonal IgG bands	[142]	Low Aβ$_{1-42}$ in MS with cognitive decline respect to control and MS with normal cognitive performance
MS with cognitive impairment	↓	↓	n.d.			
MS without cognitive impairment	↑	↓	n.d.			

ABBREVIATION: Aβ$_{42}$, Amyloid β$_{1-42}$; T-tau, total tau; p-tau, phospho tau; PGRN; progranulin; GRN, granulin; IATI, INNOTEST amyloid-tau index; AD, Alzheimer's Disease; MCI, Mild Cognitive Impairment; FTD Fronto Temporal Dementia; VaD Vascular Dementia; CADASIL, Cerebral Autosomal Dominant Arteriopathy with Subcortical Infarcts and Leukoencephalopathy; PD, Parkinson Disease; PDD Parkinson disease with dementia; LBD, Lewy Body Disease; CJD, Creutzfeldt-Jakob Disease; MS, Multiple Sclerosis.

Novel Candidate Biomarkers

For many neurological diseases, the efficacy and outcome of treatment depend on early detection. Diagnosis is currently based on the observation of clinical symptoms and neuroimaging abnormalities, which appear at relatively late stages in the pathogenesis; so the discovery of an early marker of the disease is auspicable. In the last decade, microRNAs (miRNAs), short non-coding RNAs that post-transcriptionally regulate messenger RNA (mRNA), have gained significant attention as key players involved in nervous system development, physiology, and disease [33]. Recently, stable circulating forms of miRNAs have been isolated from several human body fluids and, while their biological significance remains unclear, they have been implicated as novel disease biomarkers [11, 14, 169, 170]. Circulating miRNAs can be detected in peripheral tissues and can be used to "capture" changes in the cell of origin, including neurons. This has generated substantial interest in the use of miRNAs as biomarkers for CNS pathology, such as Alzheimer's disease and multiple sclerosis [171].

Another emerging biomarker in MS is kFLC Index: a quantitative assay to monitor variation in intrathecal Ig synthesis that provides a valid aid in the diagnosis of this pathology [135]. More validation is needed to confirm its prognostic value and eventual treatment response.

Recent research has reported the existence of a new class of neuropeptides, called orexins or hypocretins, which are produced by a small group of neurons in the hypothalamus. Narcolepsy with cataplexy is a sleep dysregulation disorder with alterations of REM sleep, i.e., sleep onset REM periods and REM sleep instability. Deficient orexin-A (hypocretin-1) signaling is assumed to be a major cause of narcolepsy with cataplexy so these patients have reduced or absent orexin-A concentrations in the CSF [172]. For this reason the dosage of orexin-A can be a good marker for narcolepsy diagnosis.

Neurofilaments (Nf) are proteins of axonal cytoskeleton, the major components in large myelinated axons [173]. They are composed of three subunits: light (NfL), medium (NfM), and heavy (NfH) chain and released into the CSF as effect of axonal damage. Nf are emerging as biomarkers in MS because their levels are related to the pathological process, and above all they seem to be useful in monitoring the treatment efficacy, as Nf specifically decreases CSF of the patient in response to treatment with natalizumab [174] and rituximab [175]. In this view, measurement of level of Nf in CSF could represent an important biomarker for therapeutic monitoring and prognostic stratification, but should be validated in randomized trials [176-178].

Mutations in the Nf heavy chain gene are found in approximately 1% of sporadic ALS and might be a risk factor for ALS [179]. Phosphorylated NfH is increased in the CSF in some ALS patients due to the degeneration of the motor neurons [180].

References

[1] Hajdu S. A note from History: Discovery of the Cerebrospinal Fluid. *Annals of Clinical & Laboratory Science,* 2003. 33, 334-36.

[2] Andreasen N, Minthon L, Davidsson P, Vanmechelen E, Vanderstichele H, Winblad B, et al. Evaluation of CSF-tau and CSF-Abeta42 as diagnostic markers for Alzheimer disease in clinical practice. *Arch Neurol,* 2001. 58, 373-9.

[3]   Bibl M, Esselmann H, and Wiltfang J. Neurochemical biomarkers in Alzheimer's disease and related disorders. *Ther Adv Neurol Disord,* 2012. 5, 335-48.

[4]   Engelborghs S and Le Bastard N. The impact of cerebrospinal fluid biomarkers on the diagnosis of Alzheimer's disease. *Mol Diagn Ther,* 2012. 16, 135-41.

[5]   Schoonenboom NS, Mulder C, Vanderstichele H, Van Elk EJ, Kok A, Van Kamp GJ, et al. Effects of processing and storage conditions on amyloid beta (1-42) and tau concentrations in cerebrospinal fluid: implications for use in clinical practice. *Clin Chem,* 2005. 51, 189-95.

[6]   Perret-Liaudet A, Pelpel M, Tholance Y, Dumont B, Vanderstichele H, Zorzi W, et al. Risk of Alzheimer's disease biological misdiagnosis linked to cerebrospinal collection tubes. *J Alzheimers Dis,* 2012. 31, 13-20.

[7]   Sancesario GM, Esposito Z, Nuccetelli M, Bernardini S, Sorge R, Martorana A, et al. Abeta1-42 Detection in CSF of Alzheimer's disease is influenced by temperature: indication of reversible Abeta1-42 aggregation? *Exp Neurol,* 2010. 223, 371-6.

[8]   Vanderstichele H, Bibl M, Engelborghs S, Le Bastard N, Lewczuk P, Molinuevo JL, et al. Standardization of preanalytical aspects of cerebrospinal fluid biomarker testing for Alzheimer's disease diagnosis: a consensus paper from the Alzheimer's Biomarkers Standardization Initiative. *Alzheimers Dement,* 2012. 8, 65-73.

[9]   Del Campo M, Mollenhauer B, Bertolotto A, Engelborghs S, Hampel H, Simonsen AH, et al. Recommendations to standardize preanalytical confounding factors in Alzheimer's and Parkinson's disease cerebrospinal fluid biomarkers: an update. *Biomark Med,* 2012. 6, 419-30.

[10]   Mattsson N, Andreasson U, Persson S, Carrillo MC, Collins S, Chalbot S, et al. CSF biomarker variability in the Alzheimer's Association quality control program. *Alzheimers Dement,* 2013. 9, 251-61.

[11]   Watson MA and Scott MG. Clinical utility of biochemical analysis of cerebrospinal fluid. *Clin Chem,* 1995. 41, 343-60.

[12]   Reiber H. Flow rate of cerebrospinal fluid (CSF)--a concept common to normal blood-CSF barrier function and to dysfunction in neurological diseases. *J Neurol Sci,* 1994. 122, 189-203.

[13]   Thompson E. *The CSF protein: A Biochemical Approach.* 1988: Amsterdam, Netherlands: Elsevier

[14] Reiber H, Walther K, and Althaus H. Beta-trace protein as sensitive marker for CSF rhinorhea and CSF otorhea. *Acta Neurol Scand,* 2003. 108, 359-62.

[15] Kaplan SL. Clinical presentations, diagnosis, and prognostic factors of bacterial meningitis. *Infect Dis Clin North Am,* 1999. 13, 579-94, vi-vii.

[16] Wubbel L and Mccracken GH, Jr. Management of bacterial meningitis: 1998. *Pediatr Rev,* 1998. 19, 78-84.

[17] Read SJ and Kurtz JB. Laboratory diagnosis of common viral infections of the central nervous system by using a single multiplex PCR screening assay. *J Clin Microbiol,* 1999. 37, 1352-5.

[18] Zunt JR and Marra CM. Cerebrospinal fluid testing for the diagnosis of central nervous system infection. *Neurol Clin,* 1999. 17, 675-89.

[19] Nanos NE and Delanghe JR. Evaluation of Sysmex UF-1000i for use in cerebrospinal fluid analysis. *Clin Chim Acta,* 2008. 392, 30-3.

[20] Chanteau S, Dartevelle S, Mahamane AE, Djibo S, Boisier P, and Nato F. New rapid diagnostic tests for Neisseria meningitidis serogroups A, W135, C, and Y. *PLoS Med,* 2006. 3, e337.

[21] Tanel RE, Kao SY, Niemiec TM, Loeffelholz MJ, Holland DT, Shoaf LA, et al. Prospective comparison of culture vs genome detection for diagnosis of enteroviral meningitis in childhood. *Arch Pediatr Adolesc Med,* 1996. 150, 919-24.

[22] Ramers C, Billman G, Hartin M, Ho S, and Sawyer MH. Impact of a diagnostic cerebrospinal fluid enterovirus polymerase chain reaction test on patient management. *JAMA,* 2000. 283, 2680-5.

[23] Jeffery KJ, Read SJ, Peto TE, Mayon-White RT, and Bangham CR. Diagnosis of viral infections of the central nervous system: clinical interpretation of PCR results. *Lancet,* 1997. 349, 313-7.

[24] Garcia-Monco JC. Central nervous system tuberculosis. *Neurol Clin,* 1999. 17, 737-59.

[25] Weller PF and Liu LX. Eosinophilic meningitis. *Semin Neurol,* 1993. 13, 161-8.

[26] Nathoo N, Nadvi SS, Narotam PK, and Van Dellen JR. Brain abscess: management and outcome analysis of a computed tomography era experience with 973 patients. *World Neurosurg,* 2011. 75, 716-26; discussion 612-7.

[27] Asbury AK and Cornblath DR. Assessment of current diagnostic criteria for Guillain-Barre syndrome. *Ann Neurol,* 1990. 27 Suppl, S21-4.

[28] Dalmau J, Gleichman AJ, Hughes EG, Rossi JE, Peng X, Lai M, et al. Anti-NMDA-receptor encephalitis: case series and analysis of the effects of antibodies. *Lancet Neurol,* 2008. 7, 1091-8.

[29] Lai M, Huijbers MG, Lancaster E, Graus F, Bataller L, Balice-Gordon R, et al. Investigation of LGI1 as the antigen in limbic encephalitis previously attributed to potassium channels: a case series. *Lancet Neurol,* 2010. 9, 776-85.

[30] Lancaster E, Huijbers MG, Bar V, Boronat A, Wong A, Martinez-Hernandez E, et al. Investigations of caspr2, an autoantigen of encephalitis and neuromyotonia. *Ann Neurol,* 2011. 69, 303-11.

[31] Hacohen Y, Wright S, Waters P, Agrawal S, Carr L, Cross H, et al. Paediatric autoimmune encephalopathies: clinical features, laboratory investigations and outcomes in patients with or without antibodies to known central nervous system autoantigens. *J Neurol Neurosurg Psychiatry,* 2013. 84, 748-55.

[32] Dalmau J, Lancaster E, Martinez-Hernandez E, Rosenfeld MR, and Balice-Gordon R. Clinical experience and laboratory investigations in patients with anti-NMDAR encephalitis. *Lancet Neurol,* 2011. 10, 63-74.

[33] Lai M, Hughes EG, Peng X, Zhou L, Gleichman AJ, Shu H, et al. AMPA receptor antibodies in limbic encephalitis alter synaptic receptor location. *Ann Neurol,* 2009. 65, 424-34.

[34] Lancaster E, Lai M, Peng X, Hughes E, Constantinescu R, Raizer J, et al. Antibodies to the GABA(B) receptor in limbic encephalitis with seizures: case series and characterisation of the antigen. *Lancet Neurol,* 2010. 9, 67-76.

[35] Clarke JL, Perez HR, Jacks LM, Panageas KS, and Deangelis LM. Leptomeningeal metastases in the MRI era. *Neurology,* 2010. 74, 1449-54.

[36] Chamberlain MC. Leptomeningeal metastases in the MRI era. *Neurology,* 2011. 76, 200; author reply 200-1.

[37] Groves MD. New strategies in the management of leptomeningeal metastases. *Arch Neurol,* 2010. 67, 305-12.

[38] Glass JP, Melamed M, Chernik NL, and Posner JB. Malignant cells in cerebrospinal fluid (CSF): the meaning of a positive CSF cytology. *Neurology,* 1979. 29, 1369-75.

[39] Wasserstrom WR, Glass JP, and Posner JB. Diagnosis and treatment of leptomeningeal metastases from solid tumors: experience with 90 patients. *Cancer,* 1982. 49, 759-72.

[40] Corsini E, Bernardi G, Gaviani P, Silvani A, De Grazia U, Ciusani E, et al. Intrathecal synthesis of tumor markers is a highly sensitive test in the diagnosis of leptomeningeal metastasis from solid cancers. *Clin Chem Lab Med,* 2009. 47, 874-9.

[41] Herrlinger U, Wiendl H, Renninger M, Forschler H, Dichgans J, and Weller M. Vascular endothelial growth factor (VEGF) in leptomeningeal metastasis: diagnostic and prognostic value. *Br J Cancer,* 2004. 91, 219-24.

[42] Groves MD, Hess KR, Puduvalli VK, Colman H, Conrad CA, Gilbert MR, et al. Biomarkers of disease: cerebrospinal fluid vascular endothelial growth factor (VEGF) and stromal cell derived factor (SDF)-1 levels in patients with neoplastic meningitis (NM) due to breast cancer, lung cancer and melanoma. *J Neurooncol,* 2009. 94, 229-34.

[43] Hutterer M, Medinger M, and Untergasser GEA. Dickkopf-3 (DKK-3) protein in cerebrospinal fluid (CSF): A biomarker for neoplastic meningitis? *J ClinOncol* 2010. 28, Abstract e12517.

[44] Hegde U, Filie A, Little RF, Janik JE, Grant N, Steinberg SM, et al. High incidence of occult leptomeningeal disease detected by flow cytometry in newly diagnosed aggressive B-cell lymphomas at risk for central nervous system involvement: the role of flow cytometry versus cytology. *Blood,* 2005. 105, 496-502.

[45] Quijano S, Lopez A, Manuel Sancho J, Panizo C, Deben G, Castilla C, et al. Identification of leptomeningeal disease in aggressive B-cell non-Hodgkin's lymphoma: improved sensitivity of flow cytometry. *J Clin Oncol,* 2009. 27, 1462-9.

[46] Tormey W, O'shea P, and Brennan P. National guidelines for analysis of cerebrospinal fluid for bilirubin in suspected subarachnoid haemorrhage. *Ann Clin Biochem,* 2012. 49, 102-3.

[47] Frank RA, Galasko D, Hampel H, Hardy J, De Leon MJ, Mehta PD, et al. Biological markers for therapeutic trials in Alzheimer's disease. Proceedings of the biological markers working group; NIA initiative on neuroimaging in Alzheimer's disease. *Neurobiol Aging,* 2003. 24, 521-36.

[48] Duranti F, Pieri M, Centonze D, Buttari F, Bernardini S, and Dessi M. Determination of kFLC and K Index in cerebrospinal fluid: a valid alternative to assess intrathecal immunoglobulin synthesis. *J Neuroimmunol,* 2013. 263, 116-20.

[49] Albert MS, Dekosky ST, Dickson D, Dubois B, Feldman HH, Fox NC, et al. The diagnosis of mild cognitive impairment due to Alzheimer's

disease: recommendations from the National Institute on Aging-Alzheimer's Association workgroups on diagnostic guidelines for Alzheimer's disease. *Alzheimers Dement,* 2011. 7, 270-9.

[50] Dubois B, Feldman HH, Jacova C, Dekosky ST, Barberger-Gateau P, Cummings J, et al. Research criteria for the diagnosis of Alzheimer's disease: revising the NINCDS-ADRDA criteria. *Lancet Neurol,* 2007. 6, 734-46.

[51] Mckhann GM, Knopman DS, Chertkow H, Hyman BT, Jack CR, Jr., Kawas CH, et al. The diagnosis of dementia due to Alzheimer's disease: recommendations from the National Institute on Aging-Alzheimer's Association workgroups on diagnostic guidelines for Alzheimer's disease. *Alzheimers Dement,* 2011. 7, 263-9.

[52] Hsich G, Kenney K, Gibbs CJ, Lee KH, and Harrington MG. The 14-3-3 brain protein in cerebrospinal fluid as a marker for transmissible spongiform encephalopathies. *N Engl J Med,* 1996. 335, 924-30.

[53] Ghidoni R, Stoppani E, Rossi G, Piccoli E, Albertini V, Paterlini A, et al. Optimal plasma progranulin cutoff value for predicting null progranulin mutations in neurodegenerative diseases: a multicenter Italian study. *Neurodegener Dis,* 2012. 9, 121-7.

[54] Braak H and Braak E. Diagnostic criteria for neuropathologic assessment of Alzheimer's disease. *Neurobiol Aging,* 1997. 18, S85-8.

[55] Davies L, Wolska B, Hilbich C, Multhaup G, Martins R, Simms G, et al. A4 amyloid protein deposition and the diagnosis of Alzheimer's disease: prevalence in aged brains determined by immunocytochemistry compared with conventional neuropathologic techniques. *Neurology,* 1988. 38, 1688-93.

[56] Fagan AM, Roe CM, Xiong C, Mintun MA, Morris JC, and Holtzman DM. Cerebrospinal fluid tau/beta-amyloid(42) ratio as a prediction of cognitive decline in nondemented older adults. *Arch Neurol,* 2007. 64, 343-9.

[57] Lanari A and Parnetti L. Cerebrospinal fluid biomarkers and prediction of conversion in patients with mild cognitive impairment: 4-year follow-up in a routine clinical setting. *ScientificWorldJournal,* 2009. 9, 961-6.

[58] Hertze J, Minthon L, Zetterberg H, Vanmechelen E, Blennow K, and Hansson O. Evaluation of CSF biomarkers as predictors of Alzheimer's disease: a clinical follow-up study of 4.7 years. *J Alzheimers Dis,* 2010. 21, 1119-28.

[59] Perrin RJ, Fagan AM, and Holtzman DM. Multimodal techniques for diagnosis and prognosis of Alzheimer's disease. *Nature,* 2009. 461, 916-22.

[60] Hansson O, Zetterberg H, Buchhave P, Londos E, Blennow K, and Minthon L. Association between CSF biomarkers and incipient Alzheimer's disease in patients with mild cognitive impairment: a follow-up study. *Lancet Neurol,* 2006. 5, 228-34.

[61] Holland D, Brewer JB, Hagler DJ, Fennema-Notestine C, and Dale AM. Subregional neuroanatomical change as a biomarker for Alzheimer's disease. *Proc Natl Acad Sci U S A,* 2009. 106, 20954-9.

[62] Okello A, Koivunen J, Edison P, Archer HA, Turkheimer FE, Nagren K, et al. Conversion of amyloid positive and negative MCI to AD over 3 years: an 11C-PIB PET study. *Neurology,* 2009. 73, 754-60.

[63] Alladi S, Xuereb J, Bak T, Nestor P, Knibb J, Patterson K, et al. Focal cortical presentations of Alzheimer's disease. *Brain,* 2007. 130, 2636-45.

[64] Hardy J and Selkoe DJ. The amyloid hypothesis of Alzheimer's disease: progress and problems on the road to therapeutics. *Science,* 2002. 297, 353-6.

[65] Wiltfang J, Esselmann H, Bibl M, Smirnov A, Otto M, Paul S, et al. Highly conserved and disease-specific patterns of carboxyterminally truncated Abeta peptides 1-37/38/39 in addition to 1-40/42 in Alzheimer's disease and in patients with chronic neuroinflammation. *J Neurochem,* 2002. 81, 481-96.

[66] Lewczuk P, Esselmann H, Otto M, Maler JM, Henkel AW, Henkel MK, et al. Neurochemical diagnosis of Alzheimer's dementia by CSF Abeta42, Abeta42/Abeta40 ratio and total tau. *Neurobiol Aging,* 2004. 25, 273-81.

[67] Blennow K, Vanmechelen E, and Hampel H. CSF total tau, Abeta42 and phosphorylated tau protein as biomarkers for Alzheimer's disease. *Mol Neurobiol,* 2001. 24, 87-97.

[68] Wiltfang J, Esselmann H, Maler JM, Bleich S, Huther G, and Kornhuber J. Molecular biology of Alzheimer's dementia and its clinical relevance to early diagnosis and new therapeutic strategies. *Gerontology,* 2001. 47, 65-71.

[69] Sancesario GM, Cencioni MT, Esposito Z, Borsellino G, Nuccetelli M, Martorana A, et al. The load of amyloid-beta oligomers is decreased in the cerebrospinal fluid of Alzheimer's disease patients. *J Alzheimers Dis,* 2012. 31, 865-78.

[70] Hulstaert F, Blennow K, Ivanoiu A, Schoonderwaldt HC, Riemenschneider M, De Deyn PP, et al. Improved discrimination of AD patients using beta-amyloid(1-42) and tau levels in CSF. *Neurology,* 1999. 52, 1555-62.

[71] Le Bastard N, Martin JJ, Vanmechelen E, Vanderstichele H, De Deyn PP, and Engelborghs S. Added diagnostic value of CSF biomarkers in differential dementia diagnosis. *Neurobiol Aging,* 2010. 31, 1867-76.

[72] Iqbal K and Grundke-Iqbal I. Tau phosphatase activity as a therapeutic target for AD. *Drug News Perspect,* 1998. 11, 10-4.

[73] Vanderstichele H, De Vreese K, Blennow K, Andreasen N, Sindic C, Ivanoiu A, et al. Analytical performance and clinical utility of the INNOTEST PHOSPHO-TAU181P assay for discrimination between Alzheimer's disease and dementia with Lewy bodies. *Clin Chem Lab Med,* 2006. 44, 1472-80.

[74] Parnetti L, Lanari A, Amici S, Gallai V, Vanmechelen E, and Hulstaert F. CSF phosphorylated tau is a possible marker for discriminating Alzheimer's disease from dementia with Lewy bodies. Phospho-Tau International Study Group. *Neurological Sciences,* 2001. 22, 77-8.

[75] Rascovsky K, Hodges JR, Knopman D, Mendez MF, Kramer JH, Neuhaus J, et al. Sensitivity of revised diagnostic criteria for the behavioural variant of frontotemporal dementia. *Brain,* 2011. 134, 2456-77.

[76] Mesulam MM. Slowly progressive aphasia without generalized dementia. *Ann Neurol,* 1982. 11, 592-8.

[77] Mackenzie IR, Neumann M, Bigio EH, Cairns NJ, Alafuzoff I, Kril J, et al. Nomenclature and nosology for neuropathologic subtypes of frontotemporal lobar degeneration: an update. *Acta Neuropathol,* 2010. 119, 1-4.

[78] Baker M, Mackenzie IR, Pickering-Brown SM, Gass J, Rademakers R, Lindholm C, et al. Mutations in progranulin cause tau-negative frontotemporal dementia linked to chromosome 17. *Nature,* 2006. 442, 916-9.

[79] Cruts M, Gijselinck I, Van Der Zee J, Engelborghs S, Wils H, Pirici D, et al. Null mutations in progranulin cause ubiquitin-positive frontotemporal dementia linked to chromosome 17q21. *Nature,* 2006. 442, 920-4.

[80] Hutton M, Lendon CL, Rizzu P, Baker M, Froelich S, Houlden H, et al. Association of missense and 5'-splice-site mutations in tau with the inherited dementia FTDP-17. *Nature,* 1998. 393, 702-5.

[81] Dejesus-Hernandez M, Mackenzie IR, Boeve BF, Boxer AL, Baker M, Rutherford NJ, et al. Expanded GGGGCC hexanucleotide repeat in noncoding region of C9ORF72 causes chromosome 9p-linked FTD and ALS. *Neuron,* 2011. 72, 245-56.

[82] Renton AE, Majounie E, Waite A, Simon-Sanchez J, Rollinson S, Gibbs JR, et al. A hexanucleotide repeat expansion in C9ORF72 is the cause of chromosome 9p21-linked ALS-FTD. *Neuron,* 2011. 72, 257-68.

[83] Sjogren M, Minthon L, Davidsson P, Granerus AK, Clarberg A, Vanderstichele H, et al. CSF levels of tau, beta-amyloid(1-42) and GAP-43 in frontotemporal dementia, other types of dementia and normal aging. *J Neural Transm,* 2000. 107, 563-79.

[84] Bhandari V, Palfree RG, and Bateman A. Isolation and sequence of the granulin precursor cDNA from human bone marrow reveals tandem cysteine-rich granulin domains. *Proc Natl Acad Sci U S A,* 1992. 89, 1715-9.

[85] Mackenzie IR. The neuropathology and clinical phenotype of FTD with progranulin mutations. *Acta Neuropathol,* 2007. 114, 49-54.

[86] Finch N, Baker M, Crook R, Swanson K, Kuntz K, Surtees R, et al. Plasma progranulin levels predict progranulin mutation status in frontotemporal dementia patients and asymptomatic family members. *Brain,* 2009. 132, 583-91.

[87] Hsiung GY, Fok A, Feldman HH, Rademakers R, and Mackenzie IR. rs5848 polymorphism and serum progranulin level. *J Neurol Sci,* 2011. 300, 28-32.

[88] Crystal H and Dickson D. Cerebral infarcts in patients with autopsy proven Alzheimer's disease. *Neurobiology of Aging,* 2002. 23, S54-S54.

[89] Pathological correlates of late-onset dementia in a multicentre, community-based population in England and Wales. Neuropathology Group of the Medical Research Council Cognitive Function and Ageing Study (MRC CFAS). *Lancet,* 2001. 357, 169-75.

[90] Jellinger KA and Attems J. Prevalence and pathogenic role of cerebrovascular lesions in Alzheimer disease. *J Neurol Sci,* 2005. 229-230, 37-41.

[91] Petrovitch H, Ross GW, Steinhorn SC, Abbott RD, Markesbery W, Davis D, et al. AD lesions and infarcts in demented and non-demented Japanese-American men. *Ann Neurol,* 2005. 57, 98-103.

[92] Jellinger KA. Understanding the pathology of vascular cognitive impairment. *J Neurol Sci,* 2005. 229-230, 57-63.

[93] Fernando MS and Ince PG. Vascular pathologies and cognition in a population-based cohort of elderly people. *J Neurol Sci*, 2004. 226, 13-7.

[94] Jellinger KA. The enigma of vascular cognitive disorder and vascular dementia. *Acta Neuropathol*, 2007. 113, 349-88.

[95] Waldemar G, Dubois B, Emre M, Georges J, Mckeith IG, Rossor M, et al. Recommendations for the diagnosis and management of Alzheimer's disease and other disorders associated with dementia: EFNS guideline. *Eur J Neurol*, 2007. 14, e1-26.

[96] Stefani A, Bernardini S, Panella M, Pierantozzi M, Nuccetelli M, Koch G, et al. AD with subcortical white matter lesions and vascular dementia: CSF markers for differential diagnosis. *J Neurol Sci*, 2005. 237, 83-8.

[97] Kalaria RN and Ballard C. Overlap between pathology of Alzheimer disease and vascular dementia. *Alzheimer Dis Assoc Disord*, 1999. 13 Suppl 3, S115-23.

[98] Skoog I, Vanmechelen E, Andreasson LA, Palmertz B, Davidsson P, Hesse C, et al. A population-based study of tau protein and ubiquitin in cerebrospinal fluid in 85-year-olds: relation to severity of dementia and cerebral atrophy, but not to the apolipoprotein E4 allele. *Neurodegeneration*, 1995. 4, 433-42.

[99] Andreasen N, Vanmechelen E, Van De Voorde A, Davidsson P, Hesse C, Tarvonen S, et al. Cerebrospinal fluid tau protein as a biochemical marker for Alzheimer's disease: a community based follow up study. *J Neurol Neurosurg Psychiatry*, 1998. 64, 298-305.

[100] Jia JP, Meng R, Sun YX, Sun WJ, Ji XM, and Jia LF. Cerebrospinal fluid tau, Abeta1-42 and inflammatory cytokines in patients with Alzheimer's disease and vascular dementia. *Neurosci Lett*, 2005. 383, 12-6.

[101] Arai H, Satoh-Nakagawa T, Higuchi M, Morikawa Y, Miura M, Kawakami H, et al. No increase in cerebrospinal fluid tau protein levels in patients with vascular dementia. *Neurosci Lett*, 1998. 256, 174-6.

[102] Paraskevas GP, Kapaki E, Papageorgiou SG, Kalfakis N, Andreadou E, Zalonis I, et al. CSF biomarker profile and diagnostic value in vascular dementia. *Eur J Neurol*, 2009. 16, 205-11.

[103] Paraskevas GP, Kapaki E, Liappas I, Theotoka I, Mamali I, Zournas C, et al. The diagnostic value of cerebrospinal fluid tau protein in dementing and nondementing neuropsychiatric disorders. *J Geriatr Psychiatry Neurol*, 2005. 18, 163-73.

[104] Leszek J, Malyszczak K, Janicka B, Kiejna A, and Wiak A. Total tau in cerebrospinal fluid differentiates Alzheimer's disease from vascular dementia. *Med Sci Monit*, 2003. 9, CR484-8.

[105] Nagga K, Gottfries J, Blennow K, and Marcusson J. Cerebrospinal fluid phospho-tau, total tau and beta-amyloid(1-42) in the differentiation between Alzheimer's disease and vascular dementia. *Dement Geriatr Cogn Disord*, 2002. 14, 183-90.

[106] Schonknecht P, Pantel J, Hunt A, Volkmann M, Buerger K, Hampel H, et al. Levels of total tau and tau protein phosphorylated at threonine 181 in patients with incipient and manifest Alzheimer's disease. *Neurosci Lett*, 2003. 339, 172-4.

[107] Ravaglia S, Bini P, Sinforiani E, Franciotta D, Zardini E, Tosca P, et al. Cerebrospinal fluid levels of tau phosphorylated at threonine 181 in patients with Alzheimer's disease and vascular dementia. *Neurological Sciences*, 2008. 29, 417-23.

[108] Spillantini MG and Goedert M. The alpha-synucleinopathies: Parkinson's disease, dementia with Lewy bodies, and multiple system atrophy. *Ann N Y Acad Sci*, 2000. 920, 16-27.

[109] Galvin JE, Lee VM, and Trojanowski JQ. Synucleinopathies: clinical and pathological implications. *Arch Neurol*, 2001. 58, 186-90.

[110] Yasuda T, Nakata Y, and Mochizuki H. Alpha-synuclein and neuronal cell death. *Mol Neurobiol*, 2013. 47, 466-83.

[111] Neumann M, Kahle PJ, Giasson BI, Ozmen L, Borroni E, Spooren W, et al. Misfolded proteinase K-resistant hyperphosphorylated alpha-synuclein in aged transgenic mice with locomotor deterioration and in human alpha-synucleinopathies. *J Clin Invest*, 2002. 110, 1429-39.

[112] Kramer ML and Schulz-Schaeffer WJ. Presynaptic alpha-synuclein aggregates, not Lewy bodies, cause neurodegeneration in dementia with Lewy bodies. *J Neurosci*, 2007. 27, 1405-10.

[113] Chandra S, Gallardo G, Fernandez-Chacon R, Schluter OM, and Sudhof TC. Alpha-synuclein cooperates with CSPalpha in preventing neurodegeneration. *Cell*, 2005. 123, 383-96.

[114] Burre J, Sharma M, Tsetsenis T, Buchman V, Etherton MR, and Sudhof TC. Alpha-synuclein promotes SNARE-complex assembly in vivo and in vitro. *Science*, 2010. 329, 1663-7.

[115] Darios F, Ruiperez V, Lopez I, Villanueva J, Gutierrez LM, and Davletov B. Alpha-synuclein sequesters arachidonic acid to modulate SNARE-mediated exocytosis. *EMBO Rep*, 2010. 11, 528-33.

[116] Murphy DD, Rueter SM, Trojanowski JQ, and Lee VM. Synucleins are developmentally expressed, and alpha-synuclein regulates the size of the presynaptic vesicular pool in primary hippocampal neurons. *J Neurosci,* 2000. 20, 3214-20.

[117] Cabin DE, Shimazu K, Murphy D, Cole NB, Gottschalk W, Mcilwain KL, et al. Synaptic vesicle depletion correlates with attenuated synaptic responses to prolonged repetitive stimulation in mice lacking alpha-synuclein. *J Neurosci,* 2002. 22, 8797-807.

[118] Schulz-Schaeffer WJ. The synaptic pathology of alpha-synuclein aggregation in dementia with Lewy bodies, Parkinson's disease and Parkinson's disease dementia. *Acta Neuropathol,* 2010. 120, 131-43.

[119] Mollenhauer B, Cullen V, Kahn I, Krastins B, Outeiro TF, Pepivani I, et al. Direct quantification of CSF alpha-synuclein by ELISA and first cross-sectional study in patients with neurodegeneration. *Exp Neurol,* 2008. 213, 315-25.

[120] Hong Z, Shi M, Chung KA, Quinn JF, Peskind ER, Galasko D, et al. DJ-1 and alpha-synuclein in human cerebrospinal fluid as biomarkers of Parkinson's disease. *Brain,* 2010. 133, 713-26.

[121] Mollenhauer B, Locascio JJ, Schulz-Schaeffer W, Sixel-Doring F, Trenkwalder C, and Schlossmacher MG. alpha-Synuclein and tau concentrations in cerebrospinal fluid of patients presenting with Parkinsonism: a cohort study. *Lancet Neurol,* 2011. 10, 230-40.

[122] Tokuda T, Salem SA, Allsop D, Mizuno T, Nakagawa M, Qureshi MM, et al. Decreased alpha-synuclein in cerebrospinal fluid of aged individuals and subjects with Parkinson's disease. *Biochem Biophys Res Commun,* 2006. 349, 162-6.

[123] Tateno F, Sakakibara R, Kawai T, Kishi M, and Murano T. Alpha-synuclein in the cerebrospinal fluid differentiates synucleinopathies (Parkinson Disease, dementia with Lewy bodies, multiple system atrophy) from Alzheimer disease. *Alzheimer Dis Assoc Disord,* 2012. 26, 213-6.

[124] Parnetti L, Chiasserini D, Bellomo G, Giannandrea D, De Carlo C, Qureshi MM, et al. Cerebrospinal fluid Tau/alpha-synuclein ratio in Parkinson's disease and degenerative dementias. *Mov Disord,* 2011. 26, 1428-35.

[125] Noguchi-Shinohara M, Tokuda T, Yoshita M, Kasai T, Ono K, Nakagawa M, et al. CSF alpha-synuclein levels in dementia with Lewy bodies and Alzheimer's disease. *Brain Res,* 2009. 1251, 1-6.

[126] Ohrfelt A, Grognet P, Andreasen N, Wallin A, Vanmechelen E, Blennow K, et al. Cerebrospinal fluid alpha-synuclein in neurodegenerative disorders-a marker of synapse loss? *Neurosci Lett,* 2009. 450, 332-5.

[127] Spies PE, Melis RJ, Sjogren MJ, Rikkert MG, and Verbeek MM. Cerebrospinal fluid alpha-synuclein does not discriminate between dementia disorders. *J Alzheimers Dis,* 2009. 16, 363-9.

[128] Aerts MB, Esselink RA, Abdo WF, Bloem BR, and Verbeek MM. CSF alpha-synuclein does not differentiate between Parkinsonian disorders. *Neurobiol Aging,* 2012. 33, 430 e1-3.

[129] Wills J, Jones J, Haggerty T, Duka V, Joyce JN, and Sidhu A. Elevated tauopathy and alpha-synuclein pathology in postmortem Parkinson's disease brains with and without dementia. *Exp Neurol,* 2010. 225, 210-8.

[130] Clinton LK, Blurton-Jones M, Myczek K, Trojanowski JQ, and Laferla FM. Synergistic Interactions between Abeta, tau, and alpha-synuclein: acceleration of neuropathology and cognitive decline. *J Neurosci,* 2010. 30, 7281-9.

[131] Kasuga K, Tokutake T, Ishikawa A, Uchiyama T, Tokuda T, Onodera O, et al. Differential levels of alpha-synuclein, beta-amyloid42 and tau in CSF between patients with dementia with Lewy bodies and Alzheimer's disease. *J Neurol Neurosurg Psychiatry,* 2010. 81, 608-10.

[132] Compta Y, Marti MJ, Ibarretxe-Bilbao N, Junque C, Valldeoriola F, Munoz E, et al. Cerebrospinal tau, phospho-tau, and beta-amyloid and neuropsychological functions in Parkinson's disease. *Mov Disord,* 2009. 24, 2203-10.

[133] Sanchez-Juan P, Green A, Ladogana A, Cuadrado-Corrales N, Saanchez-Valle R, Mitrovaa E, et al. CSF tests in the differential diagnosis of Creutzfeldt-Jakob disease. *Neurology,* 2006. 67, 637-43.

[134] World Health Organization. Manual for strengthening diagnosis and surveillance of Creutzfeldt-Jakob disease. Geneva, Switzerland: WHO. 1998.

[135] Duranti F, Pieri M, Centonze D, Buttari F, Bernardini S, and Dessi M. Determination of kFLC and K Index in cerebrospinal fluid: A valid alternative to assessintrathecal immunoglobulin synthesis. *J Neuroimmunol,* 2013. 263, 116-20.

[136] Arneth B and Birklein F. High sensitivity of free lambda and free kappa light chains for detection of intrathecal immunoglobulin synthesis in cerebrospinal fluid. *Acta Neurol Scand,* 2009. 119, 39-44.

[137] Desplat-Jego S, Feuillet L, Pelletier J, Bernard D, Cherif AA, and Boucraut J. Quantification of immunoglobulin free light chains in cerebrospinal fluid by nephelometry. *J Clin Immunol,* 2005. 25, 338-45.

[138] Fischer C, Arneth B, Koehler J, Lotz J, and Lackner KJ. Kappa free light chains in cerebrospinal fluid as markers of intrathecal immunoglobulin synthesis. *Clin Chem,* 2004. 50, 1809-13.

[139] Presslauer S, Milosavljevic D, Brucke T, Bayer P, and Hubl W. Elevated levels of kappa free light chains in CSF support the diagnosis of multiple sclerosis. *J Neurol,* 2008. 255, 1508-14.

[140] Teunissen CE, Dijkstra C, and Polman C. Biological markers in CSF and blood for axonal degeneration in multiple sclerosis. *Lancet Neurol,* 2005. 4, 32-41.

[141] Khademi M, Dring AM, Gilthorpe JD, Wuolikainen A, Al Nimer F, Harris RA, et al. Intense inflammation and nerve damage in early multiple sclerosis subsides at older age: a reflection by cerebrospinal fluid biomarkers. *PLoS One,* 2013. 8, e63172.

[142] Mori F, Rossi S, Sancesario G, Codeca C, Mataluni G, Monteleone F, et al. Cognitive and cortical plasticity deficits correlate with altered amyloid-beta CSF levels in multiple sclerosis. *Neuropsychopharmacology,* 2011. 36, 559-68.

[143] Eisen A. Amyotrophic lateral sclerosis: A 40-year personal perspective. *J Clin Neurosci,* 2009. 16, 505-12.

[144] Mcgeer PL and Mcgeer EG. Inflammatory processes in amyotrophic lateral sclerosis. *Muscle Nerve,* 2002. 26, 459-70.

[145] Tarasiuk J, Kulakowska A, Drozdowski W, Kornhuber J, and Lewczuk P. CSF markers in amyotrophic lateral sclerosis. *J Neural Transm,* 2012. 119, 747-57.

[146] Kokic AN, Stevic Z, Stojanovic S, Blagojevic DP, Jones DR, Pavlovic S, et al. Biotransformation of nitric oxide in the cerebrospinal fluid of amyotrophic lateral sclerosis patients. *Redox Rep,* 2005. 10, 265-70.

[147] Kuzma M, Jamrozik Z, and Baranczyk-Kuzma A. Activity and expression of glutathione S-transferase pi in patients with amyotrophic lateral sclerosis. *Clin Chim Acta,* 2006. 364, 217-21.

[148] Tohgi H, Abe T, Yamazaki K, Murata T, Ishizaki E, and Isobe C. Increase in oxidized NO products and reduction in oxidized glutathione in cerebrospinal fluid from patients with sporadic form of amyotrophic lateral sclerosis. *Neurosci Lett,* 1999. 260, 204-6.

[149] Devos D, Moreau C, Lassalle P, Perez T, De Seze J, Brunaud-Danel V, et al. Low levels of the vascular endothelial growth factor in CSF from early ALS patients. *Neurology,* 2004. 62, 2127-9.

[150] Kuncl RW, Bilak MM, Bilak SR, Corse AM, Royal W, and Becerra SP. Pigment epithelium-derived factor is elevated in CSF of patients with amyotrophic lateral sclerosis. *J Neurochem,* 2002. 81, 178-84.

[151] Calingasan NY, Chen J, Kiaei M, and Beal MF. Beta-amyloid 42 accumulation in the lumbar spinal cord motor neurons of amyotrophic lateral sclerosis patients. *Neurobiol Dis,* 2005. 19, 340-7.

[152] Fagnart OC, Sindic CJ, and Laterre C. Free kappa and lambda light chain levels in the cerebrospinal fluid of patients with multiple sclerosis and other neurological diseases. *J Neuroimmunol,* 1988. 19, 119-32.

[153] Bracco F, Gallo P, Menna R, Battistin L, and Tavolato B. Free light chains in the CSF in multiple sclerosis. *J Neurol,* 1987. 234, 303-7.

[154] Jensen M, Basun H, and Lannfelt L. Increased cerebrospinal fluid tau in patients with Alzheimer's disease. *Neurosci Lett,* 1995. 186, 189-91.

[155] Vigo-Pelfrey C, Seubert P, Barbour R, Blomquist C, Lee M, Lee D, et al. Elevation of microtubule-associated protein tau in the cerebrospinal fluid of patients with Alzheimer's disease. *Neurology,* 1995. 45, 788-93.

[156] De Meyer G, Shapiro F, Vanderstichele H, Vanmechelen E, Engelborghs S, De Deyn PP, et al. Diagnosis-independent Alzheimer disease biomarker signature in cognitively normal elderly people. *Arch Neurol,* 2010. 67, 949-56.

[157] Riemenschneider M, Lautenschlager N, Wagenpfeil S, Diehl J, Drzezga A, and Kurz A. Cerebrospinal fluid tau and beta-amyloid 42 proteins identify Alzheimer disease in subjects with mild cognitive impairment. *Arch Neurol,* 2002. 59, 1729-34.

[158] Buchhave P, Minthon L, Zetterberg H, Wallin AK, Blennow K, and Hansson O. Cerebrospinal fluid levels of beta-amyloid 1-42, but not of tau, are fully changed already 5 to 10 years before the onset of Alzheimer dementia. *Arch Gen Psychiatry,* 2012. 69, 98-106.

[159] Mattsson N, Zetterberg H, Hansson O, Andreasen N, Parnetti L, Jonsson M, et al. CSF biomarkers and incipient Alzheimer disease in patients with mild cognitive impairment. *JAMA,* 2009. 302, 385-93.

[160] Davis DG, Schmitt FA, Wekstein DR, and Markesbery WR. Alzheimer neuropathologic alterations in aged cognitively normal subjects. *J Neuropathol Exp Neurol,* 1999. 58, 376-88.

[161] Bian H, Van Swieten JC, Leight S, Massimo L, Wood E, Forman M, et al. CSF biomarkers in frontotemporal lobar degeneration with known pathology. *Neurology,* 2008. 70, 1827-35.

[162] Clark CM, Xie S, Chittams J, Ewbank D, Peskind E, Galasko D, et al. Cerebrospinal fluid tau and beta-amyloid: how well do these biomarkers reflect autopsy-confirmed dementia diagnoses? *Arch Neurol,* 2003. 60, 1696-702.

[163] Irwin DJ, Trojanowski JQ, and Grossman M. Cerebrospinal fluid biomarkers for differentiation of frontotemporal lobar degeneration from Alzheimer's disease. *Front Aging Neurosci,* 2013. 5, 6.

[164] Bian H and Grossman M. Frontotemporal lobar degeneration: recent progress in antemortem diagnosis. *Acta Neuropathol,* 2007. 114, 23-9.

[165] Toledo JB, Brettschneider J, Grossman M, Arnold SE, Hu WT, Xie SX, et al. CSF biomarkers cutoffs: the importance of coincident neuropathological diseases. *Acta Neuropathol,* 2012. 124, 23-35.

[166] Parnetti L, Lanari A, Amici S, Gallai V, Vanmechelen E, and Hulstaert F. CSF phosphorylated tau is a possible marker for discriminating Alzheimer's disease from dementia with Lewy bodies. Phospho-Tau International Study Group. *Neurol Sci,* 2001. 22, 77-8.

[167] Buerger K, Otto M, Teipel SJ, Zinkowski R, Blennow K, Debernardis J, et al. Dissociation between CSF total tau and tau protein phosphorylated at threonine 231 in Creutzfeldt-Jakob disease. *Neurobiol Aging,* 2006. 27, 10-5.

[168] Coulthart MB, Jansen GH, Olsen E, Godal DL, Connolly T, Choi BC, et al. Diagnostic accuracy of cerebrospinal fluid protein markers for sporadic Creutzfeldt-Jakob disease in Canada: a 6-year prospective study. *BMC Neurol,* 2011. 11, 133.

[169] Weber JA, Baxter DH, Zhang S, Huang DY, Huang KH, Lee MJ, et al. The microRNA spectrum in 12 body fluids. *Clin Chem,* 2010. 56, 1733-41.

[170] Monteleone G, Fantini MC, Onali S, Zorzi F, Sancesario G, Bernardini S, et al. Phase I clinical trial of Smad7 knockdown using antisense oligonucleotide in patients with active Crohn's disease. *Mol Ther,* 2012. 20, 870-6.

[171] Mattson DH, Roos RP, Hopper JE, and Arnason BG. Light chain composition of CSF oligoclonal IgG bands in multiple sclerosis and subacute sclerosing panencephalitis. *J Neuroimmunol,* 1982. 3, 63-76.

[172] Nishino S, Ripley B, Overeem S, Nevsimalova S, Lammers GJ, Vankova J, et al. Low cerebrospinal fluid hypocretin (Orexin) and

altered energy homeostasis in human narcolepsy. *Ann Neurol,* 2001. 50, 381-8.

[173] Liu Q, Xie F, Alvarado-Diaz A, Smith MA, Moreira PI, Zhu X, et al. Neurofilamentopathy in neurodegenerative diseases. *Open Neurol J,* 2011. 5, 58-62.

[174] Gunnarsson M, Malmestrom C, Axelsson M, Sundstrom P, Dahle C, Vrethem M, et al. Axonal damage in relapsing multiple sclerosis is markedly reduced by natalizumab. *Ann Neurol,* 2011. 69, 83-9.

[175] Rossi S, Motta C, Studer V, Barbieri F, Buttari F, Bergami A, et al. Tumor necrosis factor is elevated in progressive multiple sclerosis and causes excitotoxic neurodegeneration. *Mult Scler,* 2013.

[176] Norgren N, Sundstrom P, Svenningsson A, Rosengren L, Stigbrand T, and Gunnarsson M. Neurofilament and glial fibrillary acidic protein in multiple sclerosis. *Neurology,* 2004. 63, 1586-90.

[177] Teunissen CE and Khalil M. Neurofilaments as biomarkers in multiple sclerosis. *Mult Scler,* 2012. 18, 552-6.

[178] Salzer J, Svenningsson A, and Sundstrom P. Neurofilament light as a prognostic marker in multiple sclerosis. *Mult Scler,* 2010. 16, 287-92.

[179] Al-Chalabi A and Miller CC. Neurofilaments and neurological disease. *Bioessays,* 2003. 25, 346-55.

[180] Brettschneider J, Petzold A, Schottle D, Claus A, Riepe M, and Tumani H. The neurofilament heavy chain (NfH) in the cerebrospinal fluid diagnosis of Alzheimer's disease. *Dement Geriatr Cogn Disord,* 2006. 21, 291-5.

In: Cerebrospinal Fluid
Editor: Lawrence E. Keen

ISBN: 978-1-63117-908-2
© 2014 Nova Science Publishers, Inc.

Chapter 3

Cerebrospinal Fluid Biochemical Markers of Cerebral Metabolism in Dogs

Alba Galán *and Beatrice E. Carletti*[†]

University of Córdoba, Córdoba, Spain

Abstract

Alterations in CSF levels of different neurotransmitters, enzymes and neuronal metabolic substrates have been found in different diseases affecting the central nervous system in dogs and cats (Di Terlizzi and Platt 2006). CSF lactate, pyruvate and lactate/pyruvate ratio have been proposed as biomarkers of brain energy metabolism in humans (Parnetti et al. 2000, Benoist et al. 2003, Djukic et al. 2012) and dogs (Pugliese et al. 2005, Galán et al. 2013). A recent study describes mean pyruvate (0.057 mM/l [0.01-0.151 mM/l]), and lactate (1.189 mM/l [0.416 – 1.850 mM/l]) concentration and L/P ratio (44.247 [6.110-161.00]) in 18 healthy dogs (Galán et al. 2013). In this study, no correlation was found between CSF lactate and pyruvate concentrations and serum lactate and pyruvate

---

[*] Alba Galán. Address: Campus Universitario Rabanales, Department of Animal Medicine and Surgery, CP 14014, Córdoba, Spain.
[†] Beatrice E. Carletti. Address: Campus Universitario Rabanales, Department of Animal Medicine and Surgery, CP 14014, Córdoba, Spain.

concentrations, CSF lactate and pyruvate concentrations and TNCC and CSF lactate and pyruvate concentrations and anesthetic time.

Traditionally, changes in concentration of these metabolites have been observed when oxidative damage, brain hypoxia or mitochondrial damage is present (Benoist et al., 2003, Pugliese et al., 2005). However, recently, lactate has been considered a central neuroprotective agent. In addition, lactate serves as a critical neuronal energy substrate with positive vasodilatory effects (Pugliese et al., 2005). Increased amounts of CSF pyruvate and lactate have been found in human patients with Alzheimer's disease (AD) and vascular dementia (Parnetti et al., 2000), and in dogs with Canine Cognitive Dysfunction (CCD) (Pugliese et al., 2005). An impaired cerebral oxidative glucose metabolism has been suspected in these contexts. It has been reported that antioxidant enriched diet leads to easier learning and memory improvements in dogs (Heath et al., 2007), and that it may be beneficial for promoting a physiologic brain aging and reducing the risk of neurodegenerative disease (Head et al. 2004, Manteca 2009). Influence of antioxidant on CSF composition has been suggested in a study evaluating healthy dogs CSF after 50 days of treatment with nutraceutical compounds (Galan et al., 2014). CSF biochemical variables such as sodium and glucose concentration were significantly increased after treatment, while lactate concentration and L/P ratio were significantly decreased. Considering that lactate concentration in the brain is dependent upon its rate of production and independent of the blood lactate concentration, the elevation of CSF glucose in the face of significantly lower lactate concentrations may reflect a brain energy metabolism improvement after nutraceutical administration.

Introduction

The cefalospinal fluid (CSF) is a product of plasma filtration and membrane secretion. In general it is clear, colourless, nearly acellular, and has a low protein concentration, various ions, enzymes, and other substances are also found in normal CSF (Di Terlizzi and Platt, 2006).

CSF function consists in hydromechanical protection of the central nervous system; it also plays a prominent role in the regulation of brain interstitial fluid homeostasis, which influences neuronal functioning (Sakkaa et al. 2011). The majority of CSF is secreted predominantly, but not exclusively, by the choroid plexuses. Brain interstitial fluid, ependyma and capillaries may also play a poorly defined role in CSF secretion. The rate of formation is approximately 0.047 mL/ min in dogs, dependent on the size of the animal,

0.017 mL/min in cats, 0.002 mL/min in rats and 0.35 mL/min in people (De Lahunta, 1983).

The formation rate is closely related to the weight of the choroid plexus and to the rate of sodium and bicarbonate ion exchange. CSF circulation from sites of secretion to sites of absorption largely depends on the arterial pulse wave. Additional factors such as respiratory waves, the subject's posture, jugular venous pressure and physical effort also modulate CSF flow dynamics and pressure.

Cranial and spinal arachnoid villi have been considered for a long time to be the predominant sites of CSF absorption into the venous outflow system. Experimental data suggest that cranial and spinal nerve sheaths, the cribriform plate and the adventitia of cerebral arteries constitute substantial pathways of CSF drainage into the lymphatic outflow system (Sakkaa et al., 2011).

Cerebellomedullary and lumbar puncture are frequently performed in clinical veterinary neurology. Because the fluid flows predominantly in a rostro-caudal direction, it is more diagnostic and therefore preferable to collect it from a site caudal to the suspected lesion (Chrisman, 1992). No more than 1 mL of CSF per 5 kg bodyweight (in dogs, cats and horses) should be collected (Di Terlizzi and Platt, 2006).

Accurate analysis of CSF provides a wide range of information about the neurological health of the patient. Similar to a complete blood count, CSF analysis has good sensitivity for the detection of disease; however, changes occurring in the CFS rarely suggest a specific diagnosis. In fact the possible abnormalities of CSF are relatively limited compared to the varieties of neurological disease that exists (Tipold, 1995; Bailey and Vernau, 1997).

The routine analysis of CSF in everyday veterinary clinic neurology includes cell number and type as well as CSF total protein. Additional information obtained from CSF protein electrophoresis and immunoglobulin determination and calculation of an albumin quota and IgG index can lend auxiliary support for the suspected mechanism of disease. Furthermore CSF antibody titers for specific organisms can be useful to confirm the presence of a nervous system infection. The normal ranges for CSF cell count usually does not exceed five cells per millilitre and total protein concentration of normal CSF is very low. Lumbosacral samples tend to have slightly higher levels compared with the cisternal samples. Typical reference ranges for dogs and cats are 10–40 mg/dL compared to 5–7 g/dL in the serum (Di Terlizzi and Platt, 2006). Albumin is the main protein in the CSF (50–70%), and normally γ-globulin levels are very low (5–12%) (Di Terlizzi and Platt, 2006). As said before, the interpretation of alterations for these parameters can only be made in the context of the differential diagnosis and they allow individual diseases to be grouped in categories such as inflammatory, neoplastic and metabolic, but infrequently prompt a precise diagnosis.

Current research in human and veterinary fields is focusing on the study of non-traditional CSF analytes that could be useful as markers of specific disease or specific metabolic condition of the brain.

Little has been published about the use of CSF enzyme, metabolites and neurotransmitter in dogs, in respect to different neurological conditions, although a small number of studies demonstrate potential usefulness of some markers.

Some example are the alteration of creatinine kinase and aspartate transaminase in myelin degeneration disorders; lactate dehydrogenase in lymphoma or inflammatory diseases; gamma amino-butyric acid (GABA) in epilepsy; glutamate levels in epilepsy and several diseases involving secondary tissue damage (Sugi et al., 1975). Recently neuronal metabolic substrates, such as lactate, pyruvate, glucose and ions have been proposed as biomarkers of brain energy metabolism in humans (Parnetti et al., 2000, Benoist et al., 2003, Djukic et al., 2012) and dogs (Pugliese et al., 2005, Galán et al., 2013). Here we summarize the available data in veterinary field regarding these chemistries, its proposed use and clinical utility.

To date, some studies have evaluated brain energy metabolism biomarkers in different pathologic processes affecting the CNS, however, reference ranges for lactate, pyruvate and L/P ratio in adult healthy dogs are limited and variable (Sugi et al., 1975, Löbert et al., 2003, Pugliese et al., 2005). Furthermore, CSF samples from healthy individuals are difficult to obtain so that reference ranges for well-controlled studies are often unavailable. A recent study by the author (Galan et al., 2013) provides basic information about normal CSF findings in clinically healthy Beagle dogs and contributes to establish the physiologic CSF lactate and pyruvate concentration and their ratio in adult dogs. A cerebellomedullary puncture was performed in eighteen healthy laboratory beagle dogs ranged from 3 to 5 years of age. All CSF samples showed values within normal limits for total nuclear cells count, red blood cells count and total proteins levels. CSF glucose, lactate and pyruvate and serum lactate and pyruvate were also analysed. Mean CSF glucose was 62.6 mg/dl (range 50–74 mg/dl), mean CSF pyruvate concentration was 0.057 mM/l (range 0.01–0.151 mM/l), mean lactate concentration was 1.189 mM/l (range 0.416–1.850 mM/l) and mean L/P ratio was 44.247 (range 6.110–161.00). Means serum lactate and pyruvate were 1.8 mM/l (1.1–2.98 mM/l) and 0.16 mM/l (0.05–0.19 mM/l) and no correlation were found between CSF and serum chemistries levels.

This is constant with other studies which describe that the concentration of lactic acid in the brain is dependent upon its rate of production and independent of blood lactate concentration (Bailey and Vernau, 1997).

CFS lactate and pyruvate levels obtained by cisternal puncture in the study by Galan and others (2013) are similar to those obtained in three control animals by Sugi and others (1975) (lactate range 1.99–2.26 mM/l and pyruvate range 0.257–0.32 mM/l), four healthy pre-exercise dogs by Löbert and others (2003) (lactate range 0.6–1.2 mM/l and pyruvate range 0.028– 0.083 mM/l) and the group of 11 young dogs (one to seven years of age) of the study by Pugliese and others (2005) (mean lactate 1.9±0.61 mM/l and pyruvate 0.19±0.07 mM/l). In human beings, a recent study to determine physiologic intervals for CSF lactate and pyruvate concentrations and CSF L/P ratios in a large, well-characterised reference population, reports CSF lactate and pyruvate levels between 1.01–2.09 mM and 0.03–0.15 mM, respectively, and 9.05–26.37 for CSF L/P ratio (Zhang and Natowicz, 2012). Furthermore some human studies support that CSF pyruvate decreases and lactate and L/P ratio increase with age (Benoist et al., 2003; Wilhelmina et al., 2012). However, in one recent study, a positive correlation has been described between the CSF pyruvate concentration and age (Zhang and Natowicz, 2012). More studies have to be performed in order to determine the real effect of the age in dogs.

The L/P ratio reflects the oxidative state of the brain and is classically considered as a marker of cytosolic redox status (NADH/NAD$^+$). Lactate and pyruvate concentrations and L/P ratio in CSF have diagnostic value in numerous primary and acquired disorders reflecting hypoxia in the central nervous system (Benoist et al., 2003). Although CSF lactate and pyruvate concentrations and their ratio appear to vary slightly with age in humans (Benoist et al., 2003), no studies have been realized in dogs. Sugi and others (1975) suggested L/P values between 6.23 and 10.39 mM/L as normal in their study control group, however to the date, there are not established values for normal L/P ratio in dogs.

Horn and Klein (2010) reported that volatile anaesthetics, but not intravenous anaesthetics, cause a specific, dose-dependent increase in extracellular lactate and pyruvate levels in a mouse brain. In veterinary medicine general anaesthesia has to be always performed to carry out a cisternal or a lumbosacral puncture. In the study by Galan and others (2013) where isofluorane was used as anaesthetic agent and medetomidine and butorfanol as preanaesthetic medication, lactate and pyruvate values are lower than in previous reports in which intravenous pentobarbital (Sugi et al., 1975) and intravenous sodium thiopental and gas anaesthesia (Pugliese et al., 2005) were used.

These results suggest that the anaesthetic protocol and intubation and extubation times may be related to CSF lactate levels, and a standardised technique may be necessary to establish physiologic CSF lactate and pyruvate concentration in dogs.

On the other hand, red blood cells in CSF cause significant increases in lactate concentrations, even more when exposed to air (Venkatesh et al., 2003). In the absence of pathological changes, the presence of erythrocytes in the CSF is most commonly iatrogenic (Di Terlizzi and Platt, 2006). Iatrogenic mild contamination of the samples should be considered related to lactate levels and, in human beings, CSF samples with red blood cells count superior to 200/µl or unknown erythrocyte count are excluded from the studies performed to define the physiologic range for lactate (Wilhelmina and others, 2012). Samples with tap bleedings must therefore be centrifuged immediately and the clear CSF transferred to a new tube to analyze later other chemistries.

Traditionally in human clinical neurology field, levels of CSF lactate may serve as predictors of morbidity and mortality when associated with status epilepticus (Calabrese et al., 1991). In addition, CSF lactic acidosis, which implies brain tissue acidosis, may play a role in the clinical course of severe head injury. Over a 4-day post-trauma period, patients with a post-traumatic brain injury and poor outcome had a higher ventricular CSF lactate level than patients with moderate disabilities or a good outcome. Serial measurements of cerebral-arterial lactate difference (the difference between jugular bulb and arterial lactate concentrations) have also been found to correlate with the severity of brain injury and outcome in patients with traumatic brain injury (Pang and Boysen, 2007).

Finally, CSF lactate levels have been shown to correlate with the presence of bacterial meningitis, although elevated lactate levels have also been reported in people with viral infections (Pang and Boysen, 2007). As D-lactate is not produced by mammalian cells and is only produced by bacterial metabolism, its presence in CSF fluid was found to be highly sensitive (92%) and specific (99%) for the presence of bacterial meningitis. To the authors' knowledge, no clinical veterinary studies have looked at CSF lactate levels in dogs or cats in association with brain or spinal cord disorders. Lactate and pyruvate levels and lactate: pyruvate ratio also reflects the oxidative state of the brain (Davis, 1990).

In people changes in CSF lactate and pyruvate concentrations may be found in some cases with mitochondrial disease and have been found increases in Alzheimer disease and vascular dementia, being significantly associated with the severity of dementia (Lying-Tunell et al., 1981, Parnetti et al., 2000).

In spite of traditional relationship between increased lactate, hypoxia and brain damage, it is recently been suggest that lactate could be considered a central neuroprotective agent, due to the astrocyte adaptation mechanism, decreasing glutamate formation and neuronal apoptosis after glutamate stimulation and increasing neuronal oxygen availability and synthesis of more ATP. Additionally, lactate participates as a critical neuronal energy substrate with positive vasodilatatory effects (Pugliese et al., 2005; Head et al., 2010).

In veterinary clinical neurology concentrations of CSF lactate were found significantly higher in a recent study that analyse CSF from clinical cases with a wide variety of pathologic neurological conditions, being lactate concentration higher in that dogs with worst neurologic score (Caines et al. 2013).

Some specific changes have also been described in dogs with severe canine cognitive dysfunction (CCD), which could be a reflection of altered brain energy metabolism. Pugliese and others (2005) found significant increases in potassium, pyruvate, and lactate concentrations in CSF of dogs presenting with CCD, and an impaired cerebral oxidative glucose metabolism has been suspected in this context.

On the other hands it has been hypothesized that a decline in cognitive function associated with aging in dogs might be preventable through dietary modifications or supplementation (Head et al., 2010; Heath et al., 2007). A wide variety of supplement therapies including nutraceuticals, herbal extracts and vitamins had been suggested to improve or prevent cognitive decline (Heath et al., 2007). Vitamins B, E, and C, carotenoids, flavonoids, phospatidilserine and omega 3 fatty acids have antioxidant properties and neuroprotective effects in dogs and humans (Milgram et al., 2005; Joseph et al. 2009). In humans with cognitive decline, administration of these compounds has been reported to improve social interactions, memory and learning (Head, 2004).

In dogs, and antioxidant enriched diet leads to rapid learning and memory improvements (Heath et al., 2007), and it has also been reported that antioxidants may be beneficial for promoting a healthy brain aging and reducing the risk of neurodegenerative disease (Head and Zicker, 2004; Head, 2009; Manteca, 2011). It has been also shown that medium-chain triglyceride supplementation improves visuospatial function and learning ability in healthy old dogs (Pan et al., 2010) In clinical practice, nutritional supplementation with antioxidant agents is recommended in older dogs even before clinical signs appear, in order to prevent and minimize a decline in cognitive function (Head and Zicker, 2004; Head, 2009; Manteca, 2011). Progress in this field is important in veterinary and human medicine, however, to the date, the impact of these compounds on the cerebral metabolism is unknown.

A study by the author (Galan et al., 2014) analyse some brain energy metabolism CSF biomarkers in 11 healthy adult dogs before and after the administration of a nutraceutical compound with the the objective to assess the effects of the administration of these compounds on CSF variables related with brain energy metabolism. CSF and serum biochemical variables as lactate, pyruvate, lactate/pyruvate ratio (L/P ratio), sodium (Na), chloride (Cl) and potassium (K) concentrations were measured in the CSF before and after the administration of a nutritional supplement that includes a variety of antioxidants and free radical scavengers, such as N-acetil cysteine, a-lipoic acid, Vitamins C and E, L-Carnitine, Co-enzyme Q10, and polyunsaturated fatty acids (PUFA, phosphatidylserine, docosahexaenoic acid [DHA], and eicosapentaenoic acid [EPA]). The results for all the analyzed CSF chemistries were within the reference limits proposed on the bibliography (Di Terlizzi and Platt, 2006; Pugliese et al., 2005; Sugi et al., 1975). Mean concentrations before the treatment were: potassium 2.96 mM/L (range 2.73–3.13), chloride 132 mM/L (range 124–141), sodium 151 mM/L (range 143–164), total protein 21 mg/dL (range 12–27), glucose 59 mg/dL (range 51–64), lactate 1.53 mM/L (range 1.25–1.85), piruvate 0.028 mM/L (range 0.011–0.151), ratio L/P 16.2 (range 10.2–128.1). While chemistries mean levels after the treatment were: potassium 3.19 mM/L (range 2.51–3.30), chloride 137 mM/L (range 119–149), sodium 160 mM/L (range 141–178), total protein 13 mg/dL (range 13–22), Glucose 73 mg/dL (range 53–83), lactate 1.21 mM/L (range 0.87–1.86), pyruvate 0.098 mM/L (range 0.025–0.176), ratio L/P 9.9 (range 4.9–90.0). CSF sodium and glucose concentration were significantly increased after fifty day of treatment with nutraceuticals, while lactate concentration and L/P ratio were significantly decreased. No other measured CSF variable showed significant differences before and after treatment. Furthermore, serum sodium and chloride concentrations were significantly increased.

The CSF glucose concentration depends on the plasma glucose concentration, the rate of glucose transport into the CSF and the metabolic rate of the CNS, only a limited amount of glucose enters the brain by diffusion (Fishman, 1992). The normal CSF glucose concentration is about 60–80% of the blood glucose concentration, reflecting in part the high metabolic rate of the central nervous system (Davson and Pollay, 1963; Rosenberg, 1990). This relation-ship is maintained in the CSF and serum values in the study by Galan and others (2014). In people, a glucose gradient has been demonstrated to exist along the neuraxis with glucose concentration decreasing from ventricular to lumbar fluid (Fishman, 1959), but there are no studies analysing the possible presence of this gradient in veterinary medicine. In the study by Galan et al. 2014 a significant increase was observed on CSF glucose concentration after treatment with nutraceuticals without significant changes on serum levels. This finding may suggest: 1) higher necessity of energy substrates on the brain tissue after administration of nutraceuticals, 2) hypoglycolytic state with decreased cerebral glucose consumption or impairment in the brain's capacity to utilize glucose and respond to insulin and insulin-like growth factor (IGF) stimulation. The last option involves a detrimental effect of nutraceuticals on the brain energy metabolism. In humans, impairments in brain insulin/IGF signaling lead to accumulation of β-amyloid protein, promote oxidative stress and deficits in energy metabolism (De la Monte 2012). AD patients were found to have lower than a normal cerebrospinal fluid level of insulin which causes chronic increase in glucose concentration and stimulates the formation of reactive oxygen species (Roriz-Filho et al. 2009).

Pugliese and others (2005) described a large variability in glucose concentration in dogs with severe cognitive deficits which related to the presence of an impaired cerebral oxidative glucose metabolism. In that study, increased in glucose concentration is observed in dogs with severe cognitive deficit with respect young dogs and light cognitive deficits dogs, however not significant differences were observed between groups. In the study by Galan and others (2014), although CSF glucose concentration after treatment with nutraceuticals was significant increased and no significant differences was observed in serum glucose between the group before treatment and the group after treatment, the size of the sample and the high variability observed in serum glucose concentration in the group before treatment disable to guarantee that the increased CSF glucose concentration would be related with nutraceuticals administration. However, due to the beneficial effects (neuro-protective and antioxidant effects) associated to the nutraceuticals on the brain tissue (Head and Zicker, 2004; Head, 2009; Manteca, 2011), it may be more likely to associate increasing CSF glucose concentration with the higher necessity of energy substrates on the brain.

Significant differences were observed for CSF lactate between groups in the study by Galan and others (2014). The elevation of CSF glucose whilst lactate was significantly decreased may reflect the presence of an active cerebral metabolism after the administration of nutraceuticals due to lactate concentration in the brain is dependent upon its rate of production and independent of the blood lactate concentration (Di Terlizzi and Platt, 2006).

Sodium is the most abundant electrolyte in the CSF, being important in transport and osmoregulation (Di Terlizzi and Platt, 2006). It is actively transported into the ventricular cavity and it seems to be involved in the formation of CSF (Chrisman, 1992). An increased neuronal activity requires increased energy metabolism to ensure Na(+), K(+)-ATPase activity to efflux sodium and entry potassium for restoring membrane polarization. So, increasing in CSF sodium concentration has been associated with better Na(+), K(+)-ATPase function (Pugliese et al. 2005). Normally, in normal brain tissue, fluctuations in electrolyte levels are limited, however an intense neuronal excitation, defective inhibition or energy failure cause extracellular potassium to rise and extracellular sodium to fall, this influences neuronal function and aggravate extracellular electrolyte altered distribution (Pugliese et al., 2005). Due to the correlation of CSF sodium level with serum sodium concentration (Di Terlizzi and Platt, 2006), the increase observed in this study on CSF sodium levels could be correlated with rising serum sodium levels.

However, direct effect of the nutritional supplement on brain tissue Na (+), K (+)-ATPase could not be rule out. Recently a beneficial effect of DHA and EPA supplementation has been associated with a normalization of fatty acids incorporation into phospholipid membranes, and with a partial restoration of Na(+), K(+)-ATPase activity in different regions of the brain of rats (Kumosani et al., 2011). In humans, essential polyunsaturated fatty acids (DHA and EPA) have been shown to modulate enzymes, channels and trans-porters, to interact with lipid bilayers and to affect metabolic pathways (Kumosani et al., 2011; Lauretani et al., 2009).

Potassium concentration is critical for neuronal function and the release of neurotransmitters. Potassium ion concentration is lower in CSF than in plasma and it is maintained within a very narrow margin. The normal CSF potassium concentration is 3 mmol/L. Changes in plasma potassium concentration have little effect on the CSF potassium levels (Rosenberg, 1990).

Even with very high potassium plasma concentrations, the CSF potassium concentration remains within the normal range (Murphy et al., 1986), because its transport across the brain blood barrier is limited. Magnesium and chloride are found at slightly higher concentrations in CSF than in plasma and both are known to play an important role in neuronal conduction (Maren, 1992). The transport of these ions between the blood and CSF does not occur exclusively by passive transport (Wood, 1983).

Brain energy metabolites as glucose, sodium, lactate and the L/P ratio in CSF showed significant differences between the group before treatment and the group after treatment in the study by Galan and others (2014), suggesting an influence of nutraceuticals' administration on CSF composition, which could reflect an improvement of brain energy metabolism. However, these results have to be interpreted with caution due to the small size of the sample.

On the other hand, the differences observed between pre- and post-therapy in CSF variables, although statistically significant, may be clinically irrelevant. Since the study only evaluated CSF changes, caution must be used when assuming that the same changes occur in brain tissue. However, one of the CSF functions consists in transport neurotransmitters and metabolites within the parenchyma, playing a role in maintaining the electrolyte balance necessary for neuronal function by acting as a chemical buffer for the parenchyma. By means of its close relationship to the extracellular fluid in the interstitial spaces, the CSF provides a more stable and closely controlled electrolyte environment than the blood plasma (Pugliese et al. 2005).

The recent increasing interest in neuronal metabolic substrates as markers of brain energy metabolism warrants further investigation into the use of CSF lactate, pyruvate and ions for diagnostic and prognostic purposes. Although the results obtained in the studies with healthy dogs may be consider as normal in adult healthy dogs, the limited number of animals included in the series make necessary further studies with standardised anaesthetic protocol and definite ranges of ages between group of animals. Further studies are necessary to define the role of these metabolites, its variation during a pathologic condition and how current therapies for neurologic diseases could interfere with its concentrations.

References

Bailey, C. S., Vernau, W., 1997. Cerebrospinal fluid. In: Kaneko, J. J., Harvey, J. W., Bruss, M. L. (Eds.), *Clinical Biochemistry of Domestic Animals*. Academic Press, New York, pp. 785–827.

Benoist, J. F., Alberti, C., Leclercq, S., et al. Cerebrospinal fluid lactate and pyruvate concentrations and their ratio in children: age-related reference intervals. *Clin. Chem.* 2003;49:487-94.

Calabrese, V. P., Gruemer, H. D., James, K., et al. Cerebrospinal fluid lactate levels and prognosis in status epilepticus. *Epilepsia* 1991; 32:816–821.

Caine, D., Sinclair, M., Wood, D., et al. Evaluation of cerebrospinal fluid lactate and plasma lactate concentrations in anesthetized dogs with and without intracranial disease. *Can. Vet. J.* 2013;77:297–302.

Chrisman, C. L. Cerebrospinal fluid analysis. *The Vet. Clin North Am. Small An. Practice* 1992; 22(4):781-810.

Davis, B. A., In: Davis, B. A. (Ed.), *Biogenic Monoamines and their Metabolites in the Urine, Plasma, and Cerebrospinal Fluid of Normal, Psychiatric, and Neurological Subjects.* 1990 CRC Press, Boca Raton, FL.

De Lahunta, A., Glass E. *Veterinary neuroanatomy and Clinical Neurology.* 3rd ed. Missouri, Sanunders-Elsevier; 2009:54-76.

De la Monte, S. M. Contributions of brain insulin resistance and deficiency in amyloid-related neurodegeneration in Alzehimer's disease. *Drugs.* 2012; 72:49-66.

DeSalles, A. A., Kontos, H. A., Becker, D. P., et al. Prognostic significance of ventricular CSF lactic acidosis in severe head injury. *J. Neurosurg.* 1986; 65:615-624.

Di Terlizzi, R., Platt, S. The function, composition and analysis of cerebrospinal fluid in companion animals: Part I-Function and Composition. *Vet. J.* 2006;172:422-431.

Djuki, M., Schulz, D., Schmidt, H., et el. Cerebrospinal fluid findings in geriatric patients from 2008 to 2011. *Zeistchrift fur Gerontologie und Geriatrie* 2012; 46:353–357.

Galán, A., Carletti, B.E., Morgaz, et al. Cerebrospinal fluid lactate and pyruvate concentration and their ratio in healthy adult dogs. *Vet. Rec.* 2013; 173(10):249.

Galán, A., Carletti, B.E., Morgaz, J, et al. Comparative study of the cerebrospinal fluid of healthy dogs before and after treatment with nutraceuticals. *Vet. Clin. Pathol.* 2014; 43:172-77.

Heath, S. E., Barabas, S., Craze, P. G. Nutritional supplementation in cases of canine cognitive dysfunction - A clinical trial. *Appl. Anim. Behav. Scien.* 2007:105;284-296.

Head, E., Zicker, S. C. Nutraceuticals, aging, and cognitive dysfunction. *Vet. Clin. North Am. Small Anim. Pract.* 2004;34:217-28.

Head, E. Oxidative damage and cognitive dysfunction:antioxidant treatment to promote healthy brain aging. *Neurochem. Res.* 2009;34:670-678.

Head, E. Neurobiology of the aging dog. *Age.* 2010;33:485-496.

Joseph, J., Cole, G., Head, E.,et al. Nutrition, brain aging, and neurodegeneration. *J. Neurosci.* 2009; 14;29(41):12795-801.

Horn, T., Klein, J. lactate levels in the brain are elevated upon exposure to volatile anesthetics: a microdialysis study. *Neurochem. Int.* 2010; 57:940–947.

Kumosani, T. A., Moselhy, S. S. Modulatory effect of cod-liver oil on Na(+)-K(+) ATPase in rats' brain. *Hum. Exp. Toxicol.* 2011;30:267-74.

Lauretani, F., Maggio, M., Pizzarelli, F., et al. Omega-3 and renal function in older adults.*Curr. Pharm. Des.* 2009;15:4149-4156.

Lying-Tunell, U., Lindblad, B. S., Malmlund, H. O., et al. Cerebral blood flow and metabolic rate of oxygen, glucose, lactate, pyruvate, ketone bodies and amino acids. *Acta Neurol. Scand.* 1981;63:337-350.

Löbert, V., Mischke, R., Tipold, A. Laktat-und pyruvat-bestimmung in plasma und liquor cerebrospinalis beim hund. *Kleintierpraxis* 2003;48:735–743.

Manteca, X. Nutrition and behavior in senior dogs. *Top. Companion Anim. Med.* 2011; 26:33-36.

Milgram, N. W., Head, E., Zicker, S. C., et al. Learning ability in aged beagle dogs is preserved by behavioral enrichment and dietary fortification: a two-year longitudinal study. *Neurobiol. Aging.* 2005; 26:77–90.

Pan, Y., Larson, B., Araujo, J. A., et al. Dietary supplementation with médium-chain TAG has long-lasting cognition-enhancing effects in aged dog. *Br. J. Nut.* 2010;12:1746-1754.

Pang, D., Boysen, S. Lactate in Veterinary Critical Care: Pathophysiology and Management. *J. Am. Anim. Hosp. Assoc.* 2007;43:270-279.

Parnetti, L., Reboldi, G., Gallai, V. Cerebrospinal fluid pyruvate levels in Alzheimer's disease and vascular dementia. *Neurology.* 2000;54:735-737.

Pugliese, M., Carrasco, J. L., Andre, C., et al. Severe cognitive impairment correlates with higher cerebrospinal fluid levels of lactate and pyruvate in canine model of senile dementia. *Prog. Neuro-Psychopharm. Biol. Psych.* 2005;29:603-610.

Roriz-Filho, J., Sá-Roriz, T. M., Rosset, I., Camozzato, A. L., Santos, A. C., Chaves, M. L., Moriguti, J. C., Roriz-Cruz, M. (Pre)diabetes, brain aging, and cognition. *Biochim. Biophys. Acta.* 2009, 1792:432-43.

Sakkaa, L., Coll, G., Chazala, J., Anatomy and physiology of cerebrospinal fluid European Annals of Otorhinolaryngology, *Head and Neck diseases* 2011;128: 309-316.

Sugi, T., Fujishima, M., Omae, T. Lactate and Pyruvate Concentrations, and acid-base balance of cerebrospinal fluid in experimentally induced intracerebral and subarachnoid hemorrhage in dog. *Stroke.* 1975;6:175-719.

Tipold, A. Diagnosis of inflammatory and infectious diseases of the central nervous system in dogs: a retrospective study. *Journal of Veterinary Internal Medicine* 1995;9:304–314.

Venkatesh, B., Morgan, T. J., Boots, R. J., et al. *Interpreting csf lactic acidosis: effects of erythrocytes and air exposure. critical care and resucitation* 2003;5: 177–181.

Wilhelmina, G. L., Willwmsen, M. A., Wevers, R. A., et al. Cerebrospinal fluid glucose and lactate: age-specific reference values and implications for clinical practice. *PloS ONE* 2012;7e242745.

Zhang, W. M., Natowicz, M. R. Cerebrospinal fluid lactate and pyruvate concentration and their ratio. *Clin. Bioch.* 2012; 46:694–697.

In: Cerebrospinal Fluid
Editor: Lawrence E. Keen

ISBN: 978-1-63117-908-2
© 2014 Nova Science Publishers, Inc.

Chapter 4

Cerebrospinal Fluid: Guidance for the Selection and Interpretation of Laboratory Tests

Karina Rodríguez-Capote[*]*, Vilte E. Barakauskas,*
Mathew P. Estey and Trefor N. Higgins
DynaLIFE_DX Diagnostic Laboratory Services and
The Department of Laboratory Medicine and Pathology,
University of Alberta, Edmonton, Canada

Abstract

Examination of cerebrospinal fluid (CSF) provides important diagnostic information in a number of infectious and noninfectious disorders of the central nervous system (CNS). Rather than presenting a comprehensive overview of CSF composition, physiology and changes seen in disease, the focus of this chapter will be on providing some guidance in the selection and interpretation of laboratory tests associated with a variety of neurological conditions.

Biochemical tests such as protein and glucose are performed routinely to complement macroscopic, microscopic and cytological

[*]Corresponding author:karina.capote@dynalifedx.com.

analysisin the diagnosis of acute CNS infections. Other tests are performed in specific clinical situations, for example, detection of bilirubin to rule in/out subarachnoid hemorrhage or immunoglobulin quantitation with evaluation of oligoclonal bands in the diagnostic workup of multiple sclerosis. CSF specific proteins such as beta-2-transferrin and beta trace protein can be measured to identify CSF leakage. The last section of this chapter will discuss some emerging CSF markers with potential utility in the diagnosis of neurodegenerative diseases such as Alzheimer disease (tau protein and amyloid beta-42).

List of Common Abbreviations

AFP	Alpha-fetoprotein
APP	Amyloid precursor protein
Aβ	Amyloid beta peptides
BBB	Blood-brain barrier
β-2 trf	Beta-2-transferrin
βTP	Beta trace protein
CNS	Central nervous system
IEF	Isoelectric focusing
LD	Lactate dehydrogenase
MS	Multiple sclerosis
OCB	Oligoclonal bands
PLAP	Placental alkaline phosphatase isoenzyme
Q_{alb}	Albumin quotient
RBC	Red blood cells
SAH	Subarachnoid hemorrhage
WBC	White blood cells

Introduction

Cerebrospinal fluid (CSF) is produced in the choroid plexus of the ventricles in the brain and resembles a plasma ultrafiltrate. Transporters, channels and pinocytosis provide the means for moving small molecules and proteins from the plasma into the CSF. Only a small proportion of CSF constituents (~20%) are produced intrathecally [1]. The concentration of CSF components is thus lower when compared to plasma, and is related to molecular size: ~ 100 fold lower concentrations for large molecules like proteins and 40% lower for small molecules such as glucose [2]. There is a free and active interchange of metabolites between the brain interstitial fluid and the CSF; hence biochemical changes in the central nervous system (CNS) are expected to be mirrored in the CSF making its analysis an important diagnostic tool for CNS diseases. CSF testing, however, is performed less frequently than serum, plasma and urine testing due to the difficulty of specimen collection and the potentially hazardous nature of the sample.

CSF analysis is indicated to support the diagnosis or exclusion of CNS pathologies such as infection, subarachnoid hemorrhage, primary or metastatic neoplasias, and neurodegenerative diseases [3]. The most common method applied to obtain a CSF sample is the lumbar puncture, commonly called a spinal tap. Occasionally it may be necessary to use alternative methods of collection such as cisternal puncture, ventricular puncture or direct collection from a shunt or a drain. It is important to document the sample site because cytologic and chemical composition will vary and should be interpreted accordingly [3, 4].

The CSF specimen should be collected sequentially into three to four sterile tubes which are intended for specific uses: tube #1 for chemistry and immunology studies (0.5 to 2.0 mL); tube 2 for microbiological examination (1.0 to 3 mL); and tube 3 (0.5 to 2.0 mL) for cell count and differential and the fourth tube (0.5to 2.0 mL) for cytological analysis when malignancy is suspected. Safely, up to 20 mL of CSF may be collected. Ideally a paired serum/ plasma/ blood specimen should be obtained 2 to 4 hours before lumbar puncture to allow for blood-CSF equilibrium. The analytes measured in this sample will allow correction for potential blood contamination and it can also be used to evaluate blood-CSF barrier integrity [3]. Specimens should be sent to the clinical laboratory immediately and analyzed within 1-2 hours of collection to minimize cellular degradation [1, 3, 5].

A "basic panel" or minimal battery of tests is routinely performed in every CSF sample. This includes physical inspection, cell count, glucose, and total protein concentrations. Further testing will be dictated by the presumptive clinical diagnosis. For example if infection of the CNS is suspected, CSF should be sent for microbiological studies: smear (Gram stain or other special stains, if indicated (e.g., India ink for Cryptococcus, acid fast for tuberculosis)), cultures and/or virus-specific polymerase chain reaction, because the definitive diagnosis depends on identifying the causative organism. Guidance in the selection and interpretation of laboratory tests involving physical, chemical and electrophoretic analysis of CSF samples will be discussed here. Microbiological testing is beyond the scope of this chapter.

Physical Analysis

Appearance

Normal CSF is colorless and clear in appearance, resembling water. Deviations from this appearance are likely to have clinical significance.

Turbidity in the CSF may be due to several causes including increased number of red blood cells (RBC) or white blood cells (WBC), increased concentration of protein (>1.5 g/L), or the presence of microorganisms and thus should be investigated. CSF will appear turbid upon visual inspection with WBC counts over 200 $X10^6$/L and will appear grossly bloody when RBC are present in counts greater than 6000 $X10^6$/L [3].

The most frequently observed change in color is the manifestation of *xanthochromia*, which can result from intracranial bleeding such as subarachnoid hemorrhage (SAH). Xanthochromic CSF may be pink, orange, or yellow, depending on the timing of collection following SAH. In the first 2 to 4 hours oxyhemoglobin is released from the errant RBC and the CSF shows a pale pink to orange shade. These RBC then undergo an enzyme facilitated degradation process during which heme, the oxygen carrying moiety, is released. The heme is further degraded into bilirubin, which gives a yellow-green color, evident in the CSF from 0.5 to 3 days following SAH and it will gradually disappear over the next 8 days [3]. Heme from RBC present in the CSF due to contamination during lumbar puncture should not affect the color of the CSF because of insufficient time for degradation, provided that the sample is promptly centrifuged and removed from the cells following collection. This produces a colorless supernatant and intact RBC are observed in the CSF sediment [2, 3].

Traumatic Tap

The term "traumatic tap" is applied when blood cells are unintentionally introduced into the CSF from the blood stream during the puncture for CSF collection. A traumatic tap causing blood contamination of CSF is estimated to occur in 14–20% of lumbar punctures [6]. Distinction can be made by following these criteria:

1. The number of RBC decrease greatly between the first and last tubes collected if it is a traumatic tap, whereas the RBC count remains unchanged in SAH. The percent change in RBC count between the first and last tubes is more useful than the absolute difference in the RBC counts; a 63 % reduction has been cited as a suitable cut-off [7].
2. The CSF becomes clear after centrifugation in the case of a traumatic tap, whereas the CSF supernatant remains xanthochromic in SAH.
3. Blood does not clot in SAH.

In addition to blood contamination, other causes of CSF discoloration can make this distinction difficult. Awareness of other causes of discoloration can help when interpreting the physical appearance of CSF. These include:

- CSF protein levels higher than 1.5 g/L → Yellow-straw color [3, 8]
- Hyperbilirubinemia (serum bilirubin 171 to 256.5 μmol/L) → Yellow to yellow-green color due to bilirubin and biliverdin [3, 8]
- Purulent CSF in pyogenic meningitis → Green color [8]
- Pseudomonas aeruginosa ventriculitis → Blue-green color [9]
- Hypercarotenemia → Orange color [3, 8]
- Rifampin therapy → Red-orange color [3]
- Meningeal metastatic melanoma → Brown color from melanin [3, 8]

Microscopic

The CSF is normally acellular, however, the presence of up to 6 x10^6/L WBC and up to 5x10^6/L RBC on microscopic examination is considered normal if the sample was obtained by spinal tap. A count of 6000 x10^6/L RBC indicates a grossly bloody specimen and may invalidate other microscopic parameters. The presence of blast or malignant cells should be noted and further investigated. The CSF cell count and differential should be performed without delay since a spuriously low cell count may be obtained if measured more than 60 minutes after collection [1, 3].

Increased CSF WBC levels cannot be considered pathonogmonic of an infection; increases can occur in infectious and noninfectious inflammatory

CNS pathologies. Therefore CSF cell count must always be interpreted within the clinical context. Nevertheless, acute bacterial CNS infection usually is distinguishable from a viral infection by a high WBC count which consists predominantly of polymorphonuclear cells (neutrophils) as opposed to mononuclear (lymphocytes). Viral/ aseptic meningitis typically presents with a modest WBC count consisting mostly of lymphocytes [3].

Peripheral blood contamination adds difficulty to the interpretation of CSF cell counts. However, it has been suggested that there should be 1 or 2 WBC for every 1000 RBC in a traumatic tap if the patient's peripheral blood counts are normal [3]. The following calculation is used to correct CSF WBC counts that are falsely increased due to a traumatic tap: the blood WBC count is multiplied by the ratio of the CSF to blood RBC count. The result is the number of artificially introduced WBC. The true CSF white cell count is then calculated by subtracting the artificially introduced WBC from the actual CSF WBC count [3].

$$WBC\ (added) = WBC(blood) * RBC(CSF)/RBC(blood)$$
$$WBC\ (corrected) = WBC\ (CSF) - WBC\ (added)$$

Biochemical Analysis of CSF

Quantitative analysis of specific compounds and proteins in CSF is used to identify abnormal concentrations in the CNS and help differentiate the cause of the abnormality. Chemical and biochemical analyses are primarily undertaken to aid in the diagnosis of CNS hemorrhage, infection and inflammatory states, including demyelinating disorders. The analytical methods used are similar to those applied in serum and plasma specimens, with a few exceptions.

CSF Bilirubin

CSF bilirubin serves as a marker of SAH, and is especially useful in cases where computed tomography imaging cannot easily identify the bleed (delayed imaging, small or caudal bleeds, suboptimal images) [6, 10]. Due to the very low concentration of bilirubin in CSF, routine methods used for its measurement in serum are not sufficiently sensitive for CSF. Consequently, spectrophotometric measurement of CSF bilirubin is considered an objective and semi-quantitative alternative [10-12].

This method identifies bilirubin from other pigments based on its characteristic absorption spectrum. Briefly, oxyhemoglobin has a maximum absorption at 410-418 nm while bilirubin produces a broader peak between 450 and 460 nm [11]. When both oxyhemoglobin and bilirubin are present, a characteristic peak and shoulder are observed in the absorption spectrum, and net absorbance can be determined by their respective peak heights [13]. Retrospective analysis has identified net absorbance cut-offs with which SAH is identified using this approach [13].

CSF bilirubin, however, is not specific for SAH and results need to be interpreted on a case by case basis and correction factors applied to account for non-hemorrhagic sources. The most common confounding causes are traumatic tap, timing, total CSF protein and total serum bilirubin, also known as "the four T's" [6]

Presence of too much oxyhemoglobin caused by a traumatic tap can obscure the detection of bilirubin due to spectral overlap. A recently published modified method using multi-wavelength spectrophotometry may overcome this limitation [14]. Good practice recommendations to minimize the effect of contamination from a traumatic tap include: i) using the last CSF tube collected for spectrophotometric analysis ii) timely centrifugation of the specimen and iii) establishing oxyhemoglobin cut-off beyond which SAH cannot be definitively excluded [6, 13].

CSF proteins >1g/L can increase the absorbance at 415 nm, and should be taken into account when interpreting the results. CSF protein should be measured in the same tube used for spectrophotometric analysis. Time needed for *in vivo* conversion of hemoglobin to bilirubin as well as bilirubin stability *in vitro* must be considered when obtaining CSF samples [6, 10, 11]. Sampling 12 hours post-hemorrhage and protecting the sample from light is recommended to reduce false-negative results [6, 13].

Changes in blood-brain barrier (BBB) permeability can cause movement of bilirubin bound to proteins into the CSF, without passage of hemoglobin or RBC [13]. Application of a correction factor based on the amount of bilirubin in serum and the ratio of protein present in CSF and serum is then needed to determine the amount of CSF bilirubin due to hemorrhage [14]. Therefore, a serum sample should be drawn at the time of CSF collection.

Spectrophotometers are not available in all laboratories, preventing widespread availability of CSF bilirubin measurement. Additionally, it has been argued that even though spectral absorbance scans provide an objective assessment of xanthochromia, careful visual CSF inspection has comparable sensitivity [3].

CSF Albumin

Albumin accounts for about half of total protein in the CSF [15], and is not produced or metabolized in the CNS [2]. CSF albumin concentration will thus vary with serum albumin levels and BBB permeability. To account for serum albumin variation, the ratio of albumin in the CSF to albumin in the serum (albumin quotient, $Q_{alb,}$ or albumin index) can be calculated and provides a method-independent measure to evaluate the status of the BBB [4, 16]. Increases in the albumin index are seen in meningitis (tuberculous, bacterial and cryptococcal) and leptomeningeal metastases [4]. Increases are higher in bacterial than in viral meningitis, >15 in the former, <16 in the latter [15].

Serum albumin is commonly measured using automated chemistry analyzers by dye-binding methods such as bromocresol green or bromocresol purple [2]. Because CSF albumin concentrations are several orders of magnitude lower than those found in serum (mg/L as opposed to g/L) more sensitive methods such as immunoturbidimetry or immunonephelometry have to be utilized [2, 17]. Although in clinical practice a common cut-off for the albumin index is used (<9); method differences and other patient-specific characteristics such as age, suggest that the albumin index may vary between laboratories and patient populations [4, 18, 19].

CSF Immunoglobulins

Immunoglobulins produced in serum are present in low quantities in the CSF owing to their large size. Due to differences in molecular size and level of polymerization, IgG is more prevalent than IgA and IgM molecules. Under normal conditions, antibodies are not produced in the CNS. Intrathecal production of immunoglobulins, however, can occur due to a localized immune response or autoimmune process. The immune response in the CNS differs from systemic responses in that it lacks antibody class switching. Immune responses generating IgM antibodies in the CNS will show IgM as the main antibody in CSF for the duration of the response, which means that isolated increases in these isotypes may indicate specific neurological conditions. Intrathecal IgA production is prime in neurotuberculosis, brain abscess and adrenoleucodystrophy, while IgM production predominates in Lyme disease, mumps and non-Hodgkin's lymphoma. IgA and IgM, however, are not commonly measured in CSF [15, 20].

Methods for immunoglobulin quantification in CSF are similar to those used in serum specimens and they are based on immunoturbidimetric or immunonephelometric detection of specific antibody isotypes [17, 21]. IgG is the most commonly measured isotype in CSF and is often used to help support a diagnosis of multiple sclerosis or other demyelinating disorders. Intrathecal IgG production is seen in multiple sclerosis as well as meningoencephalitis, polyradiculities and Guillain-Barré Syndrome [22]. A ratio of CSF IgG to serum IgG (CSF IgG ratio) > 0.27 is considered increased, and this is found in a majority of multiple sclerosis patients [2].

Intrathecal Immunoglobulin Production

CSF immunoglobulin results need to be interpreted in the context of serum immunoglobulin levels and BBB status, because increased permeability will result in the transfer of systemically produced immunoglobulins to the CSF. Local production of IgG in the CNS supports a diagnosis of CSF infection or inflammation. Quantitative estimates of intrathecal production are complimentary to other investigations such as identification of oligoclonal bands by isoelectric focusing (as discussed later). Several mathematical approaches have been developed to account for transfer of IgG from the serum to the CSF to help distinguish systemic immunoglobulins from those produced locally in the CNS [16, 22-24]. These mathematical relationships produce either a unitless value or an estimation of the intrathecal production of IgG per volume or per day. A few are discussed here.

The simplest approach is to normalize the CSF IgG ratio by the albumin index, and this is termed the *IgG Index* [16]. This approach relies on the fact that there is an expected range of index values in the normal population and values above this (> 0.65 or 0.7) indicate increased intrathecal IgG production [2, 25].

$$IgG\ Index = \frac{IgG(CSF) \times Albumin\ (serum)}{IgG(serum) \times Albumin(CSF)}$$

The *IgG Synthesis Rate* adjusts IgG values measured in CSF based on serum IgG values as well as albumin in both compartments, taking into account differences in transfer across the BBB due to molecular size [25]. The synthesis rate is commonly reported by the clinical laboratory providing testing for multiple sclerosis, and a synthesis rate of > 8 mg/d is found in a majority of cases [2].

Both the IgG index and synthesis rate may not be as sensitive as isoelectric focusing for the detection of intrathecal IgG, and very low values of Q_{alb} may produce misleadingly high and low values, respectively [26]. It has been suggested that the relationship between transudated albumin and transudated IgG changes with severity of barrier damage [20, 22] and possibly the age of the patients used to determine this relationship [23]. Thus formulas employing a constant (for example, the IgG Synthesis Rate) may not perform well in the presence of blood-brain barrier impairment [23]. To overcome some of these limitations, several non-linear estimates have been proposed [22, 23]. One such example, derived by Reiber et al. describes a hyperbolic relationship between CSF IgG and Q_{alb} to estimate the relative excess of CSF IgG when compared to Q_{alb}. This relationship can be expressed graphically and 5 zones delineated to indicate serum or intrathecally derived IgG in the presence of normal or increased BBB permeability [15, 20, 27]. Controversy exists regarding the performance of various equations in different patient groups and those with severe BBB compromise. Some have suggested that the IgG Index and another equation, IgG Prod, show little correlation with the CSF/Serum albumin index when compared with other estimates [23]. As with all calculated laboratory values which depend on the analysis of multiple analytes, assay performance as well as biological variation has an effect on the values reported. For intrathecal IgG production calculations, the effects of analytical imprecision have been estimated for several equations, and while variable, in many cases contribute significant error to the calculation [22].

CSF Glucose

Glucose in the CSF is derived from the serum, although the concentration is approximately 60% of serum values (reference interval 2.2 to 4.4 mmol/L) [1]. Changes in CSF glucose can occur with changes in blood brain barrier permeability or due to consumption by cells and pathogens. For example, bacterial meningitis is often associated with decreased CSF glucose values, while glucose concentrations are not decreased in viral meningitis [8, 28].

Glucose levels, however, do not help distinguish between bacterial, fungal and tuberculous meningitis [8, 29-31].

Due to the relationship between CSF and serum glucose, it is useful to measure glucose in a paired serum sample to help rule out systemic causes of altered CSF glucose (for example, hypoglycemia or diabetes) [1]. A CSF to blood glucose ratio of <0.4 discriminate bacterial meningitis in cases of suspected CNS infection [30], although specific cut-offs differ between populations studied, and whether accurate diagnosis or screening purpose is considered [1, 32].

CSF glucose can be measured using the same methods available for serum glucose measurements on automated analyzers. In resource-limited settings "dipstick" reagents (such as those used for macroscopic/chemical evaluation of urine) that include reagent pads for semi-quantitative glucose detection, protein and leukocyte esterase measurement, have been used to help identify cases of meningitis [28, 33], although the sensitivity of this approach has been questioned in patients already receiving treatment, or those with less severe illness [34].

CSF Lactate

Lactate concentrations in CSF and serum are very similar and abnormalities under normal blood-brain-barrier conditions reflect production within the CNS, as movement from the serum is very slow. CSF lactate can be measured using methods similar to those used for blood lactate determination. Reference intervals around 1.0 to 2.0 mmol/L lactate in CSF are cited [1, 35]. CSF lactate may increase due to anaerobic glycolysis during ischemic episodes (stroke, convulsion, cerebral trauma), or due to bacterial production [1].

Concentrations ranging from 2.9 to 3.4 mmol/L have been used to identify cases of bacterial meningitis [35-37]. A recent meta-analysis conducted by Sakushima et al. demonstrated high accuracy of lactate in distinguishing bacterial from aseptic meningitis with a pooled sensitivity of 93% and a pooled specificity of 96% at a cut-off value of 3.8 mmol/L [36]. Huy et al. demonstrated in another systematic review the superiority of CSF lactate compared to other conventional markers for distinguishing bacterial meningitis from aseptic meningitis [38]. The fact that CSF to blood glucose ratio of 0.4 has similar sensitivity (91%) suggests that CSF lactate measurements are redundant, at least in the differentiation of bacterial meningitis, though they may become relevant in the absence of a paired serum specimen [1].

Elevations in CSF lactate can occur in mitochondrial disorders. Yamada et al. have suggested CSF lactate levels > 2.2 mmol/L for identifying CNS involvement in a group of pediatric patients with Leigh encephalomyelopathy, MELAS, Pearson's disease, and PDH deficiency [39]. It may also be helpful to measure pyruvate in the CSF in order to calculate a lactate to pyruvate ratio. Elevated ratios can be seen with mitochondrial disorders, and in some patients with neurological symptoms when the metabolic abnormalities may only be seen in the CSF [40].

CSF Protein

Methods used for quantification of protein in serum and plasma are unsuitable for the measurement of protein in CSF due to the significantly lower protein concentration in CSF. Urine protein methods are better suited. Normal ranges of CSF protein have been cited as 150 to 450 mg/L in adults, but vary with age.

Cut-offs of 1 to 2 g/L have been used to distinguish bacterial from aseptic meningitis, with lower cut-offs used in children [1, 41, 42]. Decreased protein in the CSF may indicate CSF leakage or volume loss [42, 43]. Elevated CSF protein can have many etiologies. It may reflect increased endothelial permeability, obstructions in CSF circulation, infection (bacterial meningitis and to a lesser extent viral meningitis), impaired resorption of CSF proteins by the arachnoid villi, or local synthesis of proteins within the central nervous system (immunoglobulins being of clinical significance) [1-3]. Increased CSF protein concentration with low WBC (cytoalbuminologic dissociation) has been associated with acute and chronic demyelinating polyneuropathies such as Guillain-Barré syndrome [5, 41, 43].

Protein concentration can be falsely elevated by the presence of RBC in a traumatic tap situation. This can be corrected by subtracting 0.01 g/L of protein for every 1×10^6/L RBC. This correction, however, is only accurate when the same tube is used for the protein and cell counts.

Seldom Used Tests

While many biochemical measurements can be made in CSF, most remain the subject of research and are not used in routine clinical care, as will be discussed in the last section of this chapter. Other analytes, while measured in the CSF, may not provide additional information beyond what can be gleaned by more conventional testing and have been abandoned. As data accumulates regarding their utility and diagnostic performance, evidence to support abandoning clinical testing or implementation of new clinical assays, becomes clearer.

CSF Lactate Dehydrogenase

Among those tests no longer measured routinely is lactate dehydrogenase (LD). Increases in total LD occur with fast cell turnover and hemolysis, limiting its usefulness in disease settings.

Increased LD, particularly the LD5 isoenzyme can be seen in patients with CNS lymphoma, but may also be increased in bacterial meningitis [44]. Isoenzyme analysis is not routinely performed, and given the lack of specificity of LD5 for CNS lymphoma, its clinical utility is questionable.

CSF Adenosine Deaminase

CSF adenosine deaminase has been used to support a diagnosis of tuberculosis [45].

This enzyme is produced by many tissues and cells and is thought to reflect the increase in activated T-lymphocytes seen in tuberculous meningitis [46]. Recent meta-analyses have called into question its clinical utility, as differences in concentration cut-offs reported in the literature result in variable test accuracy. Furthermore, since adenosine deaminase cannot distinguish between bacterial and tuberculous meningitis, it may support such a diagnosis only after the former has been ruled out [46].

CSF Alkaline Phosphatase

Measurement of other enzymes in the CSF remains an esoteric laboratory practice. For example, alkaline phosphatase determination in CSF may help identify the rare occurrence of intracranial germinoma. These tumors have been shown to produce the placental alkaline phosphatase isoenzyme (PLAP) [47-49]. A concomitant increase in serum PLAP concentration in patients with germinomas, however, suggests that serum PLAP may be used as a tumor marker as well [48].

Myelin Basic Protein

Myelin basic protein (MBP) is a component of myelin surrounding axons in the white matter of the brain and may be increased in CNS demyelinating disorders such as multiple sclerosis [50]. Concomitant measurement of MBP with oligoclonal band detection and/or IgG index did not, however, increase diagnostic performance in patients suspected of multiple sclerosis [51].

Amino Acids and Neurotransmitters

Other CSF measures may not be clinically necessary, as similar information may be gleaned from analysis of serum or blood. For example, CSF glutamine has served as an indirect marker of hyperammonemia [42, 52], although systemic causes of hyperammonemia can be assessed by measuring ammonia and liver function in blood samples. Biogenic amines such as dopamine, epinephrine and norepinephrine function as neurotransmitters in the CNS, but are not part of routine psychiatric or neurological care. Disease states associated with increases in these compounds (such as neuroblastoma or pheochromocytoma) can be identified by measuring these compounds, or their metabolites, in the blood or urine [53, 54]. Amino acid profiles in CSF are clinically needed in rare neurotransmitter disorders, where alterations in amino acid concentrations are only reflected in the CNS [40].

CSF Tumor Markers

Some authors advocate that the measurement of tumor markers such as: alpha fetoprotein (AFP); carcinoembryonic antigen; CA-15-3 and human chorionic gonadotropin (hCG) in the CSF may aid in the diagnosis of leptomeningeal metastasis [1]. Because these proteins are not expressed in brain tissue, they may be very sensitive markers for detecting metastasis in patients with known primary tumors and elevated serum markers. Patients with clinical signs of neoplastic meningitis may lack neuroradiological findings and may have negative CSF cytology results [55]. Chamberlain et al.

evaluated the use of tumor markers in the CSF of eighteen patients with a clinical diagnosis of carcinomatous meningitis but negative CSF cytology and the diagnosis was corroborated in four patients (22%) [56]. Measurement of hCG and AFP in CSF proved to be helpful in the diagnosis of germ cell tumors located in the CNS [57]. It is important to measure both serum and CSF tumor marker concentrations. If the concentration of the CSF tumor markers is greater than the serum concentration, then there is evidence of neoplastic involvement, even if the cytology is negative. In the absence of disruption of the BBB, concentrations of CSF tumor markers 2-3% of matched serum values are unlikely to be due to serum contamination or simple diffusion across the BBB [57, 58].

Electrophoretic Methods

Detection of Oligoclonal Bands in Multiple Sclerosis

Multiple sclerosis (MS) is an inflammatory neurological disorder, characterized by patchy CNS lesions resulting from the demyelination of neurons. While the exact cause of this disorder remains elusive, the majority of patients with MS exhibit clonal production of IgG within the CNS (intrathecal IgG synthesis). Thus, detection of IgG bands within the CSF, referred to as oligoclonal bands (OCB), is an important adjunct to imaging and clinical history in the diagnosis of MS [59-61].

Identification of OCB involves the separation of CSF proteins using electrophoretic methods followed by visualization of IgG through staining or immunological approaches. Because IgG present within CSF represents a combination of that filtered from the blood and that synthesized intrathecally, it is imperative to analyze CSF alongside a serum specimen collected at the same time from same patient in order to distinguish the origin of a given oligoclonal band. Those appearing in the CSF only are the result of intrathecal synthesis; whereas bands that are mirrored in both the CSF and serum reflect systemic production and passive transfer into the CSF (see below for a description of CSF OCB patterns). Accurate interpretation requires that equal concentrations of IgG in CSF and serum be analyzed.

Agarose gel electrophoresis was the first technique used to detect OCB in CSF. In this approach, proteins in paired CSF and serum specimens are separated according to charge in adjacent lanes and subsequently stained to visualize bands in the gamma region that are unique to the CSF specimen. This approach, however, has several limitations. First, limited sensitivity of protein staining often yields few weakly stained bands. As a result, the diagnostic sensitivity for multiple sclerosis is suboptimal, with estimates ranging from 45-77% [62]. Second, inconsistencies in commercial agarose gel plates have been observed [62, 63]. Finally, protein staining is not specific for IgG, other proteins such as γ-trace protein may appear as CSF-specific OCB, thus confounding the interpretation [63]. The use of IgG immunofixation instead of total protein staining improves detection of oligoclonal bands, and is much more specific for IgG [62].

OCB can also be identified by isoelectric focusing (IEF) followed by IgG immunodetection. Briefly, proteins are first electrophoresed in a pH gradient, allowing for separation based on isoelectric point which confers higher resolution separation compared to agarose gel electrophoresis. In a second step, immunodetection by blotting or fixation, IgG bands are specifically detected through incubation with labeled anti-human IgG antibodies. OCB detected by IEF are typically sharper, higher in abundance, and more easily distinguished from background polyclonal IgG compared to agarose gel electrophoresis [59, 64]. As a result, the diagnostic sensitivity for multiple sclerosis exceeds that of agarose gel electrophoresis, reaching ~95% [59, 63, 65, 66]. Based on this superior diagnostic performance, IEF is now widely accepted as the gold standard method for detection of CSF OCB [59-61, 63, 67]. Despite this acceptance, the 2013 College of American Pathologists M-A Survey demonstrated that only 51% of laboratories performing CSF oligoclonal band testing used IEF, with remaining 49% employing electrophoresis.

Regardless of the methodology used to detect CSF oligoclonal bands, 5 distinct types of patterns have been described [4, 59, 65, 66].

- Normal pattern without OCB → no intrathecal IgG production.
- OCB, irregularly spaced, present in CSF but absent in serum → intrathecal IgG production.
- Identical OCB in CSF and serum plus some unique OCB in CSF → systemic immune reaction (passive filtration of IgG from serum into CSF) plus intrathecal IgG production.
- Identical OCB in CSF and serum (mirror pattern) → systemic immune reaction (no intrathecal IgG production).
- Several identical bands closely spaced to each other in CSF and serum (passive filtration of monoclonal protein from serum into CSF) →

suggestive of a monoclonal gammopathy (no indication of intrathecal IgG production).

Although two consensus reports by the Consortium of Multiple Sclerosis Clinics, now Consortium of Multiple Sclerosis Centers, endorse the reporting of these five patterns [59, 68], some authors argue that that the clinical question posed by the physician is whether CSF-specific OCB are present or not [65]. It has been suggested that the additional information is less relevant, especially given that presence of the mirror bands in type 3 and type 4 patterns has no clinical implication. Consequently, interpretation could focus solely on the presence or absence of CSF-specific OCB, with mention of possible monoclonal gammopathy if suspected [65].

Another hot topic in the field relates to the number of bands to be used as the cutoff for positivity to define an oligoclonal profile suggesting MS. While there is a consensus that the presence of ten or more OCB is highly predictive of MS [69], some have suggested a threshold of two bands [65] and others have recommended four CSF-specific bands [64]. Despite this controversy, identifying CSF OCB by IEF is regarded as the single most informative laboratory test in the workup of a patient suspected of having MS [59, 69] with a diagnostic sensitivity reported to be above 95%.

While the vast majority of patients with MS have oligoclonal bands present in the CSF that are absent from serum, this finding is not specific to multiple sclerosis. Indeed, CSF-specific oligoclonal bands are observed in many other inflammatory disorders of the CNS, for example, autoimmune disorders such as systemic lupus erythematosus and Sjögren syndrome; infectious causes such as meningitis, encephalitis, neurosyphilis, and HIV infection; and hereditary disorders such as adrenoleukodystrophy. [4, 63, 66]. Thus, a positive CSF oligoclonal bands result must be interpreted in the context of the clinical picture.

Markers of CSF Leakage

CSF leakage from the nose (CSF rhinorrhea) or ear canal (CSF otorrhea) can occur as a result of head trauma, tumor, or surgery (usually spinal or neurosurgery). This provides a potential passageway for pathogens into the brain, and thus represents a critical condition with great risk of meningitis and potentially death [70]. While CSF leaks can be identified by imaging or exploratory surgery, these procedures are expensive and invasive. Testing the fluid for the presence of glucose is NOT recommended as a confirmatory test, as its diagnostic sensitivity and specificity is poor. False negative results occur with bacterial contamination and false positive results are common in diabetic patients. As such, other biomarkers of CSF leakage, such as beta-2-transferrin (β-2 trf) and beta-trace protein (βTP) are preferred to confirm this condition. These tests however are not specific for identifying the leakage site and can yield false negatives if the leak is intermittent [71].

Beta-2-transferrin (also known as asialotransferrin, CSF-specific transferrin or tau transferrin) is an isoform of the iron-binding protein transferrin that is present in significant amounts almost exclusively in the CSF [72]. As a result, detection of β-2 trf in fluid samples, such as nasal or ear fluid, serves as an inexpensive and non-invasive diagnostic marker of CSF leakage.

β-2 trf differs from other transferrin isoforms only in that it lacks the carbohydrate sialic acid [70, 73]. Consequently, it is difficult to distinguish β-2 trf from other transferrin isoforms using chemical or immunochemical approaches alone. Transferrin isoforms, however, can be separated using electrophoretic methods, and subsequently identified immunologically. Different electrophoretic techniques have been employed, including, sodium dodecyl sulfate-polyacrylamide gel electrophoresis (SDS-PAGE), agarose gel electrophoresis, immunofixation electrophoresis [70, 72, 74, 75], and capillary electrophoresis [73]. Various approaches have also been used for subsequent detection of transferrin isoforms, including immunoblotting with anti-transferrin antibodies, immunofixation with anti-transferrin antibodies followed by silver staining, and immunofixation with labeled anti-transferrin antibodies [70, 72, 74, 75]. All approaches allow for the qualitative identification of β-2 trf in body fluids, with excellent sensitivity and specificity for the diagnosis of CSF leakage [70, 72-75]. It must be noted that hemolysis can interfere with β-2 trf analysis by gel electrophoresis, making this test difficult to interpret in specimens contaminated with blood. It appears that hemolysis does not affect the interpretation by capillary electrophoresis [73].

Beta trace protein, also known as prostaglandin D synthase, is synthesized primarily in arachnoid cells, oligodendrocytes, and the choroids plexus within the CNS. βTP is also present in the human heart, testis and serum.

Measuring βTP in fluid has been demonstrated to be an accurate marker of CSF leakage, comparable to the well-established determination of β-2 trf. Immunochemical detection of this protein has been used to diagnose CSF rhinorrhea, with a reported sensitivity of 92% and specificity of 100% [71, 76-

78]. A quantitative cut-off of ≥ 1.1 mg/L indicates a high probability of CSF leakage [71, 77, 79]. βTP has the additional advantage that its determinations can be obtained rapidly and reliably using automated nephelometers and commercially available reagents whereas β-2trf depends on laborious electrophoretic techniques. It should not, however, be used in patients with renal insufficiency or those with bacterial meningitis, due to increases and decreases of βTP in serum in these conditions, respectively [71, 76, 77].

CSF Biomarkers for Neurodegenerative Diseases

Despite different clinical presentations, neurodegenerative diseases as diverse as Alzheimer's, Parkinson's, Creutzfeldt-Jakob disease (CJD), Huntington's disease and amyotrophic lateral sclerosis share common pathogenic processes involving progressive neuroaxonal damage, deposition of misfolded proteins into filamentous lesions and inflammation [80, 81]. Several laboratories have endeavored to identify proteins that might be specific for individual diseases; however this has so far not proved a simple task especially because neurodegenerative features are shared.

Emerging Markers

Candidate markers under investigation include total tau (t-tau), phosphorylated tau (p-tau), 14-3-3, heavy-chain and light-chain neurofilaments, neuron-specific enolase, and N-acetyl aspartic, S100B, isoprostanes, and amyloid beta peptides (Aβ) [82-84]. Only a few of these markers (t-tau, p-tau, Aβ and 14-3-3 protein) are ready to be translated to the clinical laboratory due to well characterized diagnostic accuracy for either disease identification, staging or prognosis and because the assays have acceptable analytical characteristics by medical laboratory standards [82-86]. These markers will be the focus of this last section.

Amyloid precursor protein (APP) functions as a cargo receptor for binding proteins during axonal transport and it is believed to have some other important neural functions including those in memory processes. Amyloid beta peptides (Aβ) are a number of fragments (36-43 amino acid residues) of the proteolytic cleavage of APP by the enzymes α-, β- and γ-secretases. From the various Aβ peptides generated, Aβ1–42 (Aβ42) is the most amyloidogenic and forms the core of neuritic plaques used to confirm a postmortem diagnosis of AD. ThusAβ has been the focus of research and test development.

Tau is an axonal cytoskeletal protein involved in microtubule assembly and stabilization necessary for axonal transport. Abnormal phosphorylation of tau (mainly at threonine 181) leads to the formation of insoluble neurofibrillary tangles seen in several neurodegenerative diseases such as Alzheimer's, Pick's disease, progressive supranuclear palsy, corticobasal degeneration, familial frontotemporal dementia and Parkinson's [87-90]. CSF t-tau concentrations in amyotrophic lateral sclerosis are controversial, with some studies reporting elevated levels, while others observed them to be normal [81].

Kang et al. recently published an excellent review summarizing the analytical performance of the most widely used immunoassay platforms for the measurement of CSF Aβ42, t-tau, and p-tau [83]. International and multidisciplinary efforts are being put forth toward the standardization of collection, handling, and storage of CSF on the road to facilitate translation into clinical practice [91, 92].

Detailed recommendations for preanalytical and analytical aspects for AD biomarker testing in CSF have been published by the Alzheimer's Biomarkers Standardization Initiative [93]. There are already several initiatives for the creation of international biobanks for the storage of CSF and blood-derivatives from neurological patients and healthy controls using standardized protocols [94].

CSF 14-3-3 Protein in the Diagnosis Creutzfeldt-Jakob Disease

Prion diseases are neurodegenerative diseases with long incubation periods and hasty progressive deterioration once the clinical symptoms appear. At the present there are five prion diseases recognized affecting humans: Creutzfeldt-Jakob disease (which constitutes around 90 percent of the prion diseases), variant Creutzfeldt-Jakob disease, Gerstmann-Sträussler-Scheinker syndrome, fatal familial insomnia and Kuru.

CSF 14-3-3 protein is the test recommended by the World Health Organization for the diagnosis of CJD since 1998 [86]. A recent systematic review and meta-analysis reported a pooled sensitivity of 92 % and a specificity of 80 % for 14-3-3 protein in diagnosing sporadic CJD [95]. A negative CSF 14-3-3 protein test does not exclude the diagnosis, especially in cases of familial or non-classical CJD [96], and positive results have been reported in prion-unrelated neurological diseases [96, 97]. Therefore the search for new tests or combination of tests to improve the diagnosis of prion diseases is still ongoing.

Recently, Hamlin et al. demonstrated superior diagnostic accuracy of tau over 14-3-3 protein for CJD during a prospective study including 420 patients that later underwent a postmortem examination [85]. Consequently, the US National Prion Disease Pathology Surveillance Center now includes tau and 14-3-3 protein levels in their analysis of CSF for the diagnosis of CJD (www.cjdssurveillence.com). Other CSF biomarkers that have been proposed to aid in the diagnosis of CJD include the S100 protein, neuron-specific enolase and Aβ42 [98-101].

Practical Considerations and Concerns

Standardizing pre-analytical and analytical aspects of testing and establishing international Quality Control programs for AD CSF biomarkers is not enough to warrant the translation of these markers into the clinical laboratory. At present there are neither accepted nor significantly effective disease-modifying therapies for most neurodegenerative diseases nor prevention options for asymptomatic subjects. Testing for diseases with poor prognosis and no available therapy or cure has significant cultural, financial and ethical implications.

Conclusion

Examination of CSF provides important information to aid in narrowing down the diagnosis of severe and life-threatening conditions involving the CNS ranging from infection and inflammation to hemorrhage or CSF leakage. To maximize the information gained, it is important to properly collect the sample and to interpret results within the context of sample integrity, so that confounding factors such as blood contamination are not mistaken for pathology.

Abnormalities in single CSF markers are not specific for a particular CNS condition and sample procurement is difficult. This lack of specificity has resulted in the abandonment of many measurements in CSF, and has also made the development of new markers difficult. Using multiple techniques including macroscopic, microscopic and biochemical analyses, patterns of changes can be collated and their agreement with the presumptive diagnosis evaluated. However, due to the gravity of and difficulty in diagnosing CNS diseases, and the ability of the CSF to reflect CNS perturbation, CSF analysis remains an essential part of clinical laboratory testing.

Key Points to Remember

- Ideally a paired serum or plasma specimen should be obtained to allow for accurate interpretation of several variables.
- Increased CSF WBC levels cannot be considered pathonogmonic of an infection; increases can occur in noninfectious inflammatory CNS pathologies.
- CSF total protein content >1 g/L suggests an infectious or neoplastic process.
- CSF/serum albumin quotient allows assessment of the integrity of the BBB.
- The CSF/serum glucose ratio < 0.4 suggests an infectious process.
- CSF lactate >2.4 nmol/L suggests infection, ischemia or mitochondrial pathology.
- Identifying CSF OCB by IEF is regarded as the single most informative laboratory test in the workup of a patient suspected of having MS.
- CSF specific proteins such as beta-2-transferrin and beta trace protein can be measured to identify CSF leakage.

References

[1]   Watson MA, Scott MG. Clinical utility of biochemical analysis of cerebrospinal fluid. *Clinical Chemistry*. 1995; 41:343-60.

[2]   Burtis CA, Ashwood ER, Bruns DE. *Tietz Textbook of Clinical Chemistry and Molecular Diagnostics*. 5th ed. St. Louis, Mo.: Saunders; 2006.

[3]   Henry JB, McPherson RA, Pincus MR. *Henry's Clinical Diagnosis and Management by Laboratory Methods*. 22nd ed. Philadelphia, PA: Elsevier/Saunders; 2011. p. 1 *online resource* (xxi, 1543 p.).

[4] Deisenhammer F, Bartos A, Egg R, Gilhus NE, Giovannoni G, Rauer S, et al. Guidelines on routine cerebrospinal fluid analysis. Report from an EFNS task force. *European Journal of Neurology.* 2006;13:913-22.

[5] Yap CYF, Aw TC. Revisiting cerebrospinal fluid (CSF) examination. *Proceedings of Singapore Healthcare.* 2010; 19:355-360.

[6] Petzold A, Sharpe LT, Keir G. Spectrophotometry for cerebrospinal fluid pigment analysis. *Neurocritical Care.* 2006; 4:153-62.

[7] Czuczman AD, Thomas LE, Boulanger AB, Peak DA, Senecal EL, Brown DF, et al. Interpreting red blood cells in lumbar puncture: Distinguishing true subarachnoid hemorrhage from traumatic tap. *Academic Emergency Medicine* 2013; 20:247-56.

[8] Seehusen DA, Reeves MM, Fomin DA. *Cerebrospinal fluid analysis. American family physician.* 2003; 68:1103-8.

[9] Escota G, Como J, Kessler H. The green cerebrospinal fluid. *The American Journal of Medicine.* 2011; 124:411-3.

[10] Cruickshank AM. ACP best practice no 166: *CSF spectrophotometry in the diagnosis of subarachnoid haemorrhage.* 2001. p. 827-30.

[11] Cruickshank A, Auld P, Beetham R, Burrows G, Egner W, Holbrook I, et al. Revised national guidelines for analysis of cerebrospinal fluid for bilirubin in suspected subarachnoid haemorrhage. *Annals of Clinical Biochemistry.* 2008; 45:238-44.

[12] Group UKNEQASfIW. National guidelines for analysis of cerebrospinal fluid for bilirubin in suspected subarachnoid haemorrhage. *Annals of Clinical Biochemistry.* 2003; 40:481-8.

[13] Beetham R. CSF spectrophotometry for bilirubin--why and how? *Scandinavian Journal of Clinical and Laboratory Investigation.* 2009; 69:1-7.

[14] Smith A, Wu AH, Lynch KL, Ko N, Grenache DG. Multi-wavelength spectrophotometric analysis for detection of xanthochromia in cerebrospinal fluid and accuracy for the diagnosis of subarachnoid hemorrhage. *Clinica Chimica Acta.* 2013; 424:231-6.

[15] Regeniter A, Kuhle J, Mehling M, Moller H, Wurster U, Freidank H, et al. A modern approach to CSF analysis: Pathophysiology, clinical application, proof of concept and laboratory reporting. *Clinical Neurology and Neurosurgery.* 2009; 111:313-8.

[16] Tibbling G, Link H, Ohman S. Principles of albumin and IgG analyses in neurological disorders. I. Establishment of reference values. *Scandinavian Journal of Clinical and Laboratory Investigation.* 1977; 37: 385-90.

[17] Wise BL. The quantitation and fractionation of proteins in cerebrospinal fluid. *The American Journal of Medical Technology*. 1982; 48:821-7.

[18] Eeg-Olofsson O, Link H, Wigertz A. Concentrations of CSF proteins as a measure of blood brain barrier function and synthesis of IgG within the CNS in 'normal' subjects from the age of 6 months to 30 years. *Acta Paediatrica Scandinavica*. 1981; 70:167-70.

[19] Reiber H. Proteins in cerebrospinal fluid and blood: Barriers, CSF flow rate and source-related dynamics. *Restorative Neurology and Neuroscience*. 2003; 21:79-96.

[20] Reiber H, Peter JB. Cerebrospinal fluid analysis: Disease-related data patterns and evaluation programs. *Journal of the Neurological Sciences*. 2001; 184:101-22.

[21] Croci D, Nespolo A, Bosoni MA, Tarenghi G. A simple immunoturbidimetric method for igg and albumin quantitation in cerebrospinal fluid and serum. *Journal of Clinical Chemistry and Clinical Biochemistry*. 1989; 27:863-8.

[22] Lefvert AK, Link H. Igg production within the central nervous system: A critical review of proposed formulae. *Annals of Neurology*. 1985; 17:13-20.

[23] Blennow K, Fredman P, WallinA, Gottfries CG, Frey H, Pirttila T, et al. Formulas for the quantitation of intrathecal IgG production. Their validity in the presence of blood-brain barrier damage and their utility in multiple sclerosis. *Journal of the Neurological Sciences*. 1994; 121:90-6.

[24] Schuller EA, Benabdallah S, Sagar HJ, Reboul JA, Tompe LC. IgG synthesis within the central nervous system. Comparison of three formulas. *Archives of Neurology*. 1987; 44:600-4.

[25] Tourtellotte WW, Staugaitis SM, Walsh MJ, Shapshak P, Baumhefner RW, Potvin AR, et al. The basis of intra-blood-brain-barrier IgG synthesis. *Annals of Neurology*. 1985; 17:21-7.

[26] Livrea P, Trojano M, Simone IL, Zimatore GB, Lamontanara G, Leante R. Intrathecal igg synthesis in multiple sclerosis: Comparison between isoelectric focusing and quantitative estimation of cerebrospinal fluid IgG. *Journal of Neurology*. 1981;224:159-69.

[27] Sindic CJ, Van Antwerpen MP, Goffette S. The intrathecal humoral immune response: Laboratory analysis and clinical relevance. Clinical Chemistry and Laboratory Medicine: CCLM / FESCC. 2001;39:333-40.

[28] Moosa AA, Quortum HA, Ibrahim MD. Rapid diagnosis of bacterial meningitis with reagent strips. *Lancet*. 1995; 345:1290-1.

[29] Garges HP, Moody MA, Cotten CM, Smith PB, Tiffany KF, Lenfestey R, et al. Neonatal meningitis: What is the correlation among cerebrospinal fluid cultures, blood cultures, and cerebrospinal fluid parameters? *Pediatrics.* 2006; 117:1094-100.

[30] Straus SE, Thorpe KE, Holroyd-Leduc J. How do I perform a lumbar puncture and analyze the results to diagnose bacterial meningitis? *JAMA: The Journal of the American Medical Association.* 2006; 296: 2012-22.

[31] Tarvij Eslami S, Nassirian H, Mojgan BM, Bahieh ZZ, Elham H, Alimohamad N, et al. Comparison of cerebrospinal fluid in newborns and in infants </= 2 months old with or without meningitis. *Pediatrics International: Official Journal of the Japan Pediatric Society.* 2012; 54:336-40.

[32] Tamune H, Takeya H, Suzuki W, Tagashira Y, Kuki T, Honda H, et al. Cerebrospinal fluid/blood glucose ratio as an indicator for bacterial meningitis. *The American Journal of Emergency Medicine.* 2014; 32:263-6.

[33] Joshi D, Kundana K, Puranik A, Joshi R. Diagnostic accuracy of urinary reagent strip to determine cerebrospinal fluid chemistry and cellularity. *Journal of Neurosciences in rural practice.* 2013; 4:140-5.

[34] Molyneux E, Walsh A. Caution in the use of reagent strips to diagnose acute bacterial meningitis. *The Lancet.* 1996; 348:1170-1.

[35] Zhang WM, Natowicz MR. Cerebrospinal fluid lactate and pyruvate concentrations and their ratio. *Clinical Biochemistry.* 2013; 46:694-7.

[36] Sakushima K, Hayashino Y, Kawaguchi T, Jackson JL, Fukuhara S. Diagnostic accuracy of cerebrospinal fluid lactate for differentiating bacterial meningitis from aseptic meningitis: A meta-analysis. *The Journal of Infection.* 2011; 62:255-62.

[37] Majwala A, Burke R, Patterson W, Pinkerton R, Muzoora C, Wilson LA, et al. Handheld point-of-care cerebrospinal fluid lactate testing predicts bacterial meningitis in Uganda. *The American Journal of Tropical Medicine and Hygiene.* 2013; 88:127-31.

[38] Huy NT, Thao NT, Diep DT, Kikuchi M, Zamora J, Hirayama K. Cerebrospinal fluid lactate concentration to distinguish bacterial from aseptic meningitis: A systemic review and meta-analysis. *Critical Care.* 2010; 14:R240.

[39] Yamada K, Toribe Y, Yanagihara K, Mano T, Akagi M, Suzuki Y. Diagnostic accuracy of blood and csf lactate in identifying children with

mitochondrial diseases affecting the central nervous system. *Brain & Development.* 2012; 34:92-7.

[40] Sarafoglou K, Hoffman G. *Pediatric Endocrinology and Inborn Errors of Metabolism.* New York: McGraw-Hill Medical; 2009.

[41] White K, Ostrowski K, Maloney S, Norton R. The utility of cerebrospinal fluid parameters in the early microbiological assessment of meningitis. *Diagnostic Microbiology and Infectious Disease.* 2012; 73:27-30.

[42] Strasinger SK, Di Lorenzo MS. *Urinalysis and Body Fluids.* 5th ed. Philadelphia: F.A. Davis; 2008.

[43] Dougherty JM, Roth RM. Cerebral spinal fluid. *Emergency Medicine Clinics of North America.* 1986; 4:281-97.

[44] Scott BJ, Douglas VC, Tihan T, Rubenstein JL, Josephson SA. A systematic approach to the diagnosis of suspected central nervous system lymphoma. *JAMA Neurology.* 2013; 70:311-9.

[45] Xu HB, Jiang RH, Li L, Sha W, Xiao HP. Diagnostic value of adenosine deaminase in cerebrospinal fluid for tuberculous meningitis: A meta-analysis. *The International Journal of Tuberculosis and Lung Disease* 2010; 14:1382-7.

[46] Tuon FF, Higashino HR, Lopes MI, Litvoc MN, Atomiya AN, Antonangelo L, et al. Adenosine deaminase and tuberculous meningitis-- a systematic review with meta-analysis. *Scandinavian Journal of Infectious Diseases.* 2010; 42:198-207.

[47] Ramakrishnan S, Manifold IH, Ward AM, Forster DM. CSF placental alkaline phosphatase as marker in cranial dysgerminoma. *Lancet.* 1989; 2:225-225.

[48] Shinoda J, Yamada H, Sakai N, Ando T, Hirata T, Miwa Y. Placental alkaline phosphatase as a tumor marker for primary intracranial germinoma. *Journal of Neurosurgery.* 1988; 68:710-20.

[49] Watanabe S, Aihara Y, Kikuno A, Sato T, Komoda T, Kubo O, et al. A highly sensitive and specific chemiluminescent enzyme immunoassay for placental alkaline phosphatase in the cerebrospinal fluid of patients with intracranial germinomas. *Pediatric Neurosurgery.* 2012; 48:141-5.

[50] Giovannoni G. Multiple sclerosis cerebrospinal fluid biomarkers. *Disease Markers.* 2006; 22:187-96.

[51] Greene DN, Schmidt RL, Wilson AR, Freedman MS, Grenache DG. Cerebrospinal fluid myelin basic protein is frequently ordered but has little value: A test utilization study. *American Journal of Clinical Pathology.* 2012; 138:262-72.

[52] Smith SV, Forman DT. Laboratory analysis of cerebrospinal fluid. *Clinical Laboratory Science: Journal of the American Society for Medical Technology.* 1994; 7:32-8.

[53] Chen H, Sippel RS, O'Dorisio MS, Vinik AI, Lloyd RV, Pacak K, et al. The North American neuroendocrine tumor society consensus guideline for the diagnosis and management of neuroendocrine tumors: Pheochromocytoma, paraganglioma, and medullary thyroid cancer. *Pancreas.* 2010; 39:775-83.

[54] Goldstein DS, Eisenhofer G, Kopin IJ. Sources and significance of plasma levels of catechols and their metabolites in humans. *The Journal of Pharmacology and Experimental Therapeutics.* 2003; 305:800-11.

[55] DeAngelis LM, Boutros D. Leptomeningeal metastasis. *Cancer Investigation.* 2005; 23:145-54.

[56] Chamberlain MC. Cytologically negative carcinomatous meningitis: Usefulness of CSF biochemical markers. *Neurology.* 1998;50:1173-5.

[57] Mitsios JV, McClellan A, Brown S, Gronowski AM. Human chorionic gonadotropin and alpha-fetoprotein in cerebral spinal fluid: Method validation and retrospective review. *Clinical Biochemistry.* 2014.

[58] Le Rhun E, Taillibert S, Chamberlain MC. Carcinomatous meningitis: Leptomeningeal metastases in solid tumors. *Surgical Neurology International.* 2013; 4:S265-88.

[59] Freedman MS, Thompson EJ, Deisenhammer F, Giovannoni G, Grimsley G, Keir G, et al. Recommended standard of cerebrospinal fluid analysis in the diagnosis of multiple sclerosis: A consensus statement. *Archives of Neurology.* 2005; 62:865-70.

[60] Polman CH, Reingold SC, Banwell B, Clanet M, Cohen JA, Filippi M, et al. Diagnostic criteria for multiple sclerosis: 2010 revisions to the McDonald criteria. *Annals of Neurology.* 2011; 69:292-302.

[61] Yamout B, Alroughani R, Al-Jumah M, Khoury S, Abouzeid N, Dahdaleh M, et al. Consensus guidelines for the diagnosis and treatment of multiple sclerosis. *Current Medical Research and Opinion.* 2013; 29:611-21.

[62] Keren DF, Keren DF. *Protein Electrophoresis in Clinical Diagnosis.* London New York, NY: Arnold; Distributed in the U.S.A. by Oxford University Press; 2003.

[63] Awad A, Hemmer B, Hartung HP, Kieseier B, Bennett JL, Stuve O. Analyses of cerebrospinal fluid in the diagnosis and monitoring of multiple sclerosis. *Journal of Neuroimmunology.* 2010; 219:1-7.

[64] Fortini AS, Sanders EL, Weinshenker BG, Katzmann JA. Cerebrospinal fluid oligoclonal bands in the diagnosis of multiple sclerosis. Isoelectric focusing with IgG immunoblotting compared with high-resolution agarose gel electrophoresis and cerebrospinal fluid igg index. *American Journal of Clinical Pathology.* 2003; 120:672-5.

[65] Link H, Huang YM. Oligoclonal bands in multiple sclerosis cerebrospinal fluid: An update on methodology and clinical usefulness. *Journal of Neuroimmunology.* 2006; 180:17-28.

[66] Mehling M, Kuhle J, Regeniter A. 10 most commonly asked questions about cerebrospinal fluid characteristics in demyelinating disorders of the central nervous system. *The Neurologist.* 2008; 14:60-5.

[67] Petzold A, Keir G, Lim D, Smith M, Thompson EJ. Cerebrospinal fluid (CSF) and serum s100b: Release and wash-out pattern. *Brain Research Bulletin.* 2003; 61:281-5.

[68] Andersson M, Alvarez-Cermeno J, Bernardi G, Cogato I, Fredman P, Frederiksen J, et al. Cerebrospinal fluid in the diagnosis of multiple sclerosis: A consensus report. *Journal of Neurology, Neurosurgery, and Psychiatry.* 1994; 57:897-902.

[69] Petzold A. Intrathecal oligoclonal IgG synthesis in multiple sclerosis. *Journal of Neuroimmunology.* 2013; 262:1-10.

[70] Warnecke A, Averbeck T, Wurster U, Harmening M, Lenarz T, Stover T. Diagnostic relevance of beta2-transferrin for the detection of cerebrospinal fluid fistulas. *Archives of Otolaryngology-Head &Neck Surgery.* 2004; 130:1178-84.

[71] Risch L, Lisec I, Jutzi M, Podvinec M, Landolt H, Huber AR. Rapid, accurate and non-invasive detection of cerebrospinal fluid leakage using combined determination of beta-trace protein in secretion and serum. *Clinica Chimica Acta.* 2005; 351:169-76.

[72] Gorogh T, Rudolph P, Meyer JE, Werner JA, Lippert BM, Maune S. Separation of beta2-transferrin by denaturing gel electrophoresis to detect cerebrospinal fluid in ear and nasal fluids. *Clinical Chemistry.* 2005; 51:1704-10.

[73] Rodriguez-Capote K, Turner J, Macri J. Evaluation of a commercially available carbohydrate deficient transferrin kit to detect beta-2-transferrin in cerebrospinal fluid using capillary electrophoresis. *Clinical Biochemistry.* 2013; 46:1770-3.

[74] Kleine TO, Damm T, Althaus H. Quantification of beta-trace protein and detection of transferrin isoforms in mixtures of cerebrospinal fluid and

blood serum as models of rhinorrhea and otorrhea diagnosis. *Fresenius' Journal of Analytical Chemistry*. 2000; 366:382-6.

[75] McCudden CR, Senior BA, Hainsworth S, Oliveira W, Silverman LM, Bruns DE, et al. Evaluation of high resolution gel beta (2)-transferrin for detection of cerebrospinal fluid leak. *Clinical Chemistry and Laboratory Medicine*. 2013; 51:311-5.

[76] Lescuyer P, Auer L, Converset V, Hochstrasser DF, Landis BN, Burkhard PR. Comparison of gel-based methods for the detection of cerebrospinal fluid rhinorrhea. *Clinica Chimica Acta*. 2012;413:1145-50.

[77] Mantur M, Lukaszewicz-Zajac M, Mroczko B, Kulakowska A, Ganslandt O, Kemona H, et al. Cerebrospinal fluid leakage--reliable diagnostic methods. *Clinica Chimica Acta*. 2011; 412:837-40.

[78] Michel O, Bamborschke S, Nekic M, Bachmann G. Beta-trace protein (prostaglandin D synthase)--a stable and reliable protein in perilymph. *German Medical Science*. 2005; 3:1-6.

[79] Bachmann-Harildstad G. Diagnostic values of beta-2 transferrin and beta-trace protein as markers for cerebrospinal fluid fistula. *Rhinology*. 2008; 46:82-5.

[80] Skovronsky DM, Lee VM, Trojanowski JQ. Neurodegenerative diseases: New concepts of pathogenesis and their therapeutic implications. *Annual Review of Pathology*. 2006; 1:151-70.

[81] Tumani H, Teunissen C, Sussmuth S, Otto M, Ludolph AC, Brettschneider J. Cerebrospinal fluid biomarkers of neurodegeneration in chronic neurological diseases. *Expert Review of Molecular Diagnostics*. 2008; 8:479-94.

[82] Kang JH, Irwin DJ, Chen-Plotkin AS, Siderowf A, Caspell C, Coffey CS, et al. Association of cerebrospinal fluid beta-amyloid 1-42, t-tau, p-tau181, and alpha-synuclein levels with clinical features of drug-naive patients with early Parkinson's disease. *JAMA Neurology*. 2013; 70:1277-87.

[83] Kang JH, Korecka M, Toledo JB, Trojanowski JQ, Shaw LM. Clinical utility and analytical challenges in measurement of cerebrospinal fluid amyloid-beta(1-42) and tau proteins as Alzheimer disease biomarkers. *Clinical Chemistry*. 2013; 59:903-16.

[84] Tumani H, Hartung HP, Hemmer B, Teunissen C, Deisenhammer F, Giovannoni G, et al. Cerebrospinal fluid biomarkers in multiple sclerosis. *Neurobiology of Disease*. 2009; 35:117-27.

[85] Hamlin C, Puoti G, Berri S, Sting E, Harris C, Cohen M, et al. A comparison of tau and 14-3-3 protein in the diagnosis of Creutzfeldt-Jakob disease. *Neurology.* 2012; 79:547-52.

[86] Zeilder M, Gibbs JC, Meslin F. Who manual for strengthening diagnosis and surveillance of Creutzfeldt-Jakob disease. *WHO/EMC/ZDI/98.11* GENEVA 1998.

[87] Sharma S, Moon CS, Khogali A, Haidous A, Chabenne A, Ojo C, et al. Biomarkers in Parkinson's disease (recent update). *Neurochemistry International.* 2013; 63:201-29.

[88] Buongiorno M, Compta Y, Marti MJ. Amyloid-beta and tau biomarkers in Parkinson's disease-dementia. *Journal of the Neurological Sciences.* 2011; 310:25-30.

[89] Sjogren M, Minthon L, Davidsson P, Granerus AK, Clarberg A, Vanderstichele H, et al. CSF levels of tau, beta-amyloid (1-42) and gap-43 in frontotemporal dementia, other types of dementia and normal aging. *Journal of Neural Transmission* 2000; 107:563-79.

[90] Parnetti L, Tiraboschi P, Lanari A, Peducci M, Padiglioni C, D'Amore C, et al. Cerebrospinal fluid biomarkers in Parkinson's disease with dementia and dementia with Lewy bodies. *Biological Psychiatry.* 2008; 64:850-5.

[91] Mattsson N, Andreasson U, Persson S, Arai H, Batish SD, Bernardini S, et al. The Alzheimer's association external quality control program for cerebrospinal fluid biomarkers. *Alzheimers & Dementia.* 2011; 7:386-95 e6.

[92] Mattsson N, Andreasson U, Persson S, Carrillo MC, Collins S, Chalbot S, et al. CSF biomarker variability in the Alzheimer's association quality control program. *Alzheimers & Dementia.* 2013; 9:251-61.

[93] Vanderstichele H, Bibl M, Engelborghs S, Le Bastard N, Lewczuk P, Molinuevo JL, et al. Standardization of preanalytical aspects of cerebrospinal fluid biomarker testing for Alzheimer's disease diagnosis: A consensus paper from the Alzheimer's biomarkers standardization initiative. *Alzheimers & Dementia.* 2012; 8:65-73.

[94] Teunissen CE, Tumani H, Engelborghs S, Mollenhauer B. Biobanking of CSF: International standardization to optimise biomarker development. *Clinical Biochemistry.* 2014; 47:288-92.

[95] Muayqil T, Gronseth G, Camicioli R. Evidence-based guideline: Diagnostic accuracy of CSF 14-3-3 protein in sporadic Creutzfeldt-Jakob disease: Report of the guideline development subcommittee of the American Academy of Neurology. *Neurology.* 2012; 79:1499-506.

[96] Chapman T, McKeel DW, Jr., Morris JC. Misleading results with the 14-3-3 assay for the diagnosis of Creutzfeldt-Jakob disease. *Neurology.* 2000; 55:1396-7.

[97] Satoh J, Kurohara K, Yukitake M, Kuroda Y. The 14-3-3 protein detectable in the cerebrospinal fluid of patients with prion-unrelated neurological diseases is expressed constitutively in neurons and glial cells in culture. *European Neurology.* 1999; 41:216-25.

[98] Baldeiras IE, Ribeiro MH, Pacheco P, Machado A, Santana I, Cunha L, et al. Diagnostic value of csf protein profile in a portuguese population of SCJD patients. *Journal of Neurology.* 2009; 256:1540-50.

[99] Beaudry P, Cohen P, Brandel JP, Delasnerie-Laupretre N, Richard S, Launay JM, et al. 14-3-3 protein, neuron-specific enolase, and S-100 protein in cerebrospinal fluid of patients with Creutzfeldt-Jakob disease. *Dementia and Geriatric Cognitive Disorders.* 1999; 10:40-6.

[100] Boesenberg-Grosse C, Schulz-Schaeffer WJ, Bodemer M, Ciesielczyk B, Meissner B, Krasnianski A, et al. Brain-derived proteins in the csf: Do they correlate with brain pathology in CJD? *BMC Neurology.* 2006; 6:35.

[101] Sanchez-Juan P, Green A, Ladogana A, Cuadrado-Corrales N, Saanchez-Valle R, Mitrovaa E, et al. CSF tests in the differential diagnosis of Creutzfeldt-Jakob disease. *Neurology.* 2006; 67:637-43.

Index

A

acid, viii, 2, 3, 18, 27, 54, 64, 68, 73, 77, 88
acidic, 4, 60
acidosis, 66
active transport, 23
acute infection, 29
AD, viii, ix, 16, 21, 34, 35, 36, 37, 38, 39, 41, 42, 43, 50, 51, 52, 53, 62, 69, 93, 94, 95, 97
adaptation, 67
adenosine, 87, 100
adults, viii, 15, 22, 23, 34, 49, 73, 86
advancement(s), ix, 3, 16
adventitia, 63
agar, 25
age, 21, 22, 25, 35, 37, 39, 57, 64, 65, 71, 74, 82, 84, 86, 98
agglutination, 26
aggregation, 45, 55
aging population, 38
albumin, 18, 24, 63, 82, 83, 84, 97, 98
allele, 53
alpha-fetoprotein, 101
ALS, 40, 41, 44, 52, 58
Alzheimer Disease, viii, 16, 21, 41
amines, 88
amino, viii, 16, 64, 73, 88, 93
amino acid(s), viii, 16, 73, 88, 93
ammonia, 88

amyloid beta, x, 45, 76, 93
amyotrophic lateral sclerosis, 57, 58, 93, 94
anatomy, 17
anesthetics, 19, 72
aneurysm, 6, 14
antibody, 29, 31, 33, 63, 82, 83
antigen, 47
antioxidant, ix, 62, 67, 69, 72
antisense, 59
aorta, 6
aphasia, 51
Arboviruses, 28, 29
aseptic, 28, 80, 85, 86, 99
aseptic meningitis, 28, 80, 85, 86, 99
aspartate, 64
assessment, 2, 11, 49, 82, 96, 100
astrocytes, 4
asymptomatic, 32, 37, 41, 42, 52, 95
ATP, 67
atrophy, 38, 53, 54, 55
Australasia, 12
autoantibodies, 30
autoantigens, 47
autoimmune disease(s), 17, 30, 39
autopsy, 17, 35, 52, 59
autosomal dominant, 37
axonal degeneration, 39, 57
axons, 5, 11, 35, 44, 88

B

bacillus, 27
bacteria, 25, 26, 28, 29
barriers, 24
base, 73
BBB, 3, 18, 19, 23, 24, 40, 76, 81, 82, 83, 84, 89, 96
beneficial effect, 69, 70
benign, 32
BI, 54
bicarbonate, 63
bilirubin, x, 22, 33, 48, 76, 78, 79, 80, 81, 97
biliverdin, 79
biological markers, 48
biomarkers, vii, viii, ix, 1, 2, 3, 5, 10, 11, 12, 13, 15, 16, 17, 21, 31, 34, 35, 36, 37, 38, 40, 43, 44, 45, 49, 50, 51, 55, 57, 58, 59, 60, 61, 64, 68, 92, 95, 100, 103, 104
biopsy, 27, 34
biosynthesis, 25
bleeding, 78
blood, x, 3, 12, 17, 18, 19, 20, 22, 23, 24, 25, 37, 38, 45, 57, 62, 65, 66, 68, 69, 70, 71, 73, 76, 77, 78, 79, 80, 81, 84, 85, 88, 89, 92, 94, 95, 98, 99, 103
blood cultures, 99
blood flow, 20, 73
blood plasma, 71
blood stream, 78
blood-brain barrier, 18, 20, 81, 84, 98
body fluid, vii, viii, 15, 59, 92
bone(s), 18, 52
bone marrow, 52
brachial plexus, 3
brain, vii, viii, ix, 3, 12, 15, 16, 17, 18, 20, 27, 29, 34, 35, 37, 38, 49, 61, 62, 64, 65, 66, 67, 68, 69, 70, 71, 72, 73, 76, 83, 84, 85, 88, 91, 98, 105
brain abscess, 83
brain damage, 67
brainstem, 40
breakdown, 22, 33
breast cancer, 31, 48

C

calcium, 12
cancer, 31
candidates, ix, 16
Canine Cognitive Dysfunction, ix, 62
capillary, 18, 92, 102
carbohydrate, 92, 102
carbon, 18
carbon dioxide, 18
carcinoembryonic antigen, 88
cardiac surgery, viii, 2
carotenoids, 67
cataplexy, 44
CCD, ix, 62, 67
cDNA, 52
cell body, 38
cell death, 5, 35, 38, 41, 54
central nervous system (CNS), vii, ix, x, 2, 4, 11, 15, 16, 17, 19, 20, 22, 23, 24, 25, 27, 28, 29, 31, 33, 34, 38, 40, 44, 46, 47, 48, 61, 62, 64, 65, 68, 73, 75, 76, 77, 80, 82, 83, 85, 86, 87, 88, 89, 91, 92, 95, 96, 98, 100, 102
cerebellum, 19
cerebral arteries, 63
cerebral hemisphere, 19
cerebral herniation, 31
cerebrospinal fluid, vii, viii, ix, x, 1, 2, 5, 12, 13, 14, 15, 16, 24, 45, 46, 47, 48, 49, 50, 53, 54, 55, 56, 57, 58, 59, 60, 69, 71, 72, 73, 75, 96, 97, 98, 99, 100, 101, 102, 103, 104, 105
challenges, 103
chemical, 18, 21, 25, 71, 77, 78, 85, 92
childhood, 46
children, viii, 15, 21, 71, 86, 99
chorionic gonadotropin, 101
choroid, 18, 19, 25, 62, 63, 76
chromosome, 51, 52
circulation, 19, 63, 86
class switching, 82
classification, vii, 1, 3, 37
cleavage, 93
clinical application, 97

clinical diagnosis, 40, 77, 89
clinical presentation, 93
clinical symptoms, 31, 33, 34, 43, 94
clinical trials, viii, 5, 16, 21
closure, 7, 8
coding, 43
cognition, 53, 73
cognitive deficit(s), 69
cognitive dysfunction, ix, 16, 40, 67, 72
cognitive function, 67
cognitive impairment, viii, 16, 34, 36, 37,
    40, 43, 48, 49, 50, 52, 58, 73
cognitive performance, 40, 43
color, 25, 78, 79
commercial, 26, 27, 90
community, 52, 53
complement, x, 75
complete blood count, 63
complications, 21, 40
composition, ix, x, 18, 20, 59, 62, 71, 72,
    75, 77
compounds, ix, 62, 67, 68, 80, 88
compression, 8, 14
computed tomography, 33, 46, 80
conduction, 30, 70
Congress, 17
consciousness, 29
consensus, 33, 45, 91, 101, 102, 104
constituents, 17, 76
consumption, 69, 84
contamination, 38, 66, 77, 78, 79, 80, 81,
    89, 92, 95
control group, 38, 65
controlled studies, 64
controversial, 38, 94
convulsion, 85
correction factors, 81
correlation, vii, ix, 1, 6, 38, 61, 65, 70, 84,
    99
cortex, 40
corticobasal degeneration, 94
creatinine, 64
Creutzfeldt-Jakob disease, 34, 39, 56, 59,
    93, 94, 104, 105
cross-sectional study, 55

CSF biochemical markers, vii, 101
CSF biomarkers, vii, viii, ix, 2, 3, 12, 16,
    21, 31, 37, 40, 49, 50, 51, 58, 59, 68, 95
CT, 31, 33
CT scan, 31
culture, 26, 27, 46, 105
cure, 95
cysteine, 36, 52, 68
cytokines, 13, 40, 53
cytology, 32, 47, 48, 88
cytometry, 27, 32, 33, 48
cytoskeleton, 35, 44

D

database, 5
deaths, 29
deficiency, 72, 86
deficit, 69
degenerative dementia, 55
degradation, 77, 78
degradation process, 78
dementia, viii, 16, 34, 35, 36, 37, 39, 42, 43,
    49, 50, 51, 52, 53, 54, 55, 56, 58, 59, 67,
    94, 104
demyelination, 39, 89
Department of Labor, 75
deposition, 38, 49, 93
deposits, 35
depth, 3
derivatives, 94
destruction, 10
detectable, 105
detection, viii, x, 16, 21, 26, 27, 32, 33, 34,
    40, 43, 46, 56, 63, 76, 81, 83, 84, 85, 88,
    89, 90, 92, 97, 102, 103
diabetes, 73, 85
diabetic patients, 92
diagnostic criteria, 39, 46, 51
diagnostic markers, 44
diet, ix, 62, 67
differential diagnosis, 24, 27, 36, 37, 53, 56,
    64, 105
diffusion, 18, 19, 20, 24, 68, 89
dilation, 19

discrimination, 37, 51
disease progression, 40
diseases, vii, viii, ix, 16, 17, 24, 34, 59, 61,
    64, 71, 73, 77, 93, 94, 95, 96, 100, 103,
    105
disorder, 36, 37, 44, 53, 89
dissociation, 30, 86
distribution, 70
diversity, 36
DNA, 36
docosahexaenoic acid, 68
dogs, vii, ix, 61, 62, 63, 64, 65, 66, 67, 68,
    69, 71, 72, 73
dopamine, 88
dosage, 44
drainage, 63
drug reactions, 28

epithelium, 41, 58
Epstein-Barr virus, 27, 28
equilibrium, 77
erythrocytes, 66, 74
ethical implications, 95
ethyl alcohol, 19
etiology, 31
evidence, viii, 6, 7, 9, 10, 11, 16, 24, 31, 35,
    38, 87, 89
evoked potential, 14
evolution, 39
examinations, 10
excitability, 30, 40
excitation, 70
excitotoxicity, 40, 41
exclusion, 5, 77
exercise, 65
exocytosis, 54
exposure, 72, 74
extracts, 67

E

edema, 10
eicosapentaenoic acid, 68
electrolyte, 70, 71
electromyography, 30, 40
electrophoresis, 63, 89, 90, 92, 102
ELISA, 55
emergency, 28
EMG, 30
employment, 21
empyema, 8, 14
encephalitis, 27, 29, 47, 91
encephalopathy, 23, 39
endocrine, 24
energy, ix, 23, 60, 61, 62, 64, 67, 68, 69, 70,
    71
England, 52
enterovirus, 27, 28, 46
environment, 71
enzyme(s), viii, ix, 2, 4, 61, 62, 64, 68, 70,
    78, 87, 93, 100
enzyme immunoassay, 100
eosinophils, 23, 28
EPA, 68, 70
epilepsy, 64
epinephrine, 88

F

false negative, 92
false positive, 33, 92
family members, 52
family physician, 97
fasciculation, 40
fat, 19
fatty acids, 67, 70
fever, 29
filament, viii, 2, 9
filtration, 62, 90
financial, 95
fistulas, 102
fixation, 90
flavonoids, 67
fluctuations, 70
fluid, vii, viii, 13, 15, 16, 17, 33, 46, 49, 53,
    54, 55, 56, 58, 59, 62, 63, 66, 69, 71, 72,
    73, 74, 76, 92, 97, 98, 99, 100, 101, 102,
    103, 104
football, 3
foramen, 17
force, 97

formation, 34, 62, 63, 67, 69, 70, 94
fragments, 93
fungal infection, 24
fungi, 26, 28

G

GABA, 47, 64
gel, 89, 90, 92, 102, 103
general anaesthesia, 65
genes, 36
genetic mutations, 36
genome, 46
glial cell(s), vii, 1, 3, 40, 105
glucose, ix, x, 19, 23, 24, 29, 32, 62, 64, 67,
    68, 69, 70, 73, 74, 75, 77, 84, 85, 92, 96,
    99
glutamate, 40, 64, 67
glutamine, 88
glutathione, 40, 57
glycolysis, 85
grading, 3, 10, 12
gravity, 96
growth, 26, 31, 41, 48, 58, 69
growth factor, 31, 41, 48, 58, 69
guidance, vii, x, 75
guidelines, 3, 21, 33, 48, 49, 97, 101
Guillain-Barre syndrome, 46

H

head injury, 66, 72
head trauma, 91
headache, 21, 29
health, 63
heme, 78
hemoglobin, 22, 81
hemorrhage, 2, 21, 22, 23, 33, 76, 80, 81, 95
herpes, 26, 27
herpes simplex, 26, 27
herpes simplex virus type 1, 27
heterogeneity, 38, 41
history, 17, 33, 40, 89
HIV, 28, 91

HIV/AIDS, 28
homeostasis, 17, 18, 60, 62
horses, 63
human, viii, ix, 2, 3, 6, 7, 8, 9, 10, 11, 12,
    13, 33, 43, 52, 54, 55, 60, 62, 64, 65, 66,
    68, 88, 90, 92
human body, 33, 43
human chorionic gonadotropin, 88
human subjects, 8
hydrocephalus, 17
hydrogen, 40
hydrogen peroxide, 40
hypoglycemia, 23, 85
hypothalamus, 44
hypothesis, 41, 50
hypoxia, ix, 3, 62, 65, 67

I

iatrogenic, 66
ideal, viii, 2, 5
identification, 26, 27, 28, 35, 39, 83, 92, 93
images, 80
immune reaction, 90
immune response, 82, 98
immune system, 40
immunofixation, 90, 92
immunoglobulin(s), ix, x, 16, 40, 48, 56, 57,
    63, 76, 82, 83, 86
immunotherapy, 30
impairments, 69
improvements, ix, 62, 67
in vitro, 54, 81
in vivo, 16, 34, 35, 36, 39, 54, 81
incidence, 3, 48
incubation period, 94
India, 77
individuals, 36, 55, 64
induction, 8
infants, 99
infection, 22, 23, 27, 28, 29, 30, 46, 63, 77,
    79, 80, 83, 85, 86, 91, 95, 96
inflammation, 24, 39, 57, 83, 93, 95
inflammatory disease, 24, 64
inflammatory mediators, 40

influenza, 26
ingestion, 22
inhibition, 70
injury(s), vii, 1, 2, 3, 4, 5, 6, 9, 10, 12, 13, 14, 37, 66
insomnia, 94
institutions, 2
insulin, 69, 72
insulin resistance, 72
integrin, 31
integrity, 24, 77, 95, 96
intervention, 2, 27
intracerebral hemorrhage, 22
intracranial pressure, 30, 31
intravenously, 26
ions, 18, 62, 64, 70, 71
iron, 92
ischemia, 4, 14, 20, 96

J

Japan, 99
Jefferson, Thomas, 1

L

laboratory tests, vii, x, 75, 77
lactate dehydrogenase, 32, 64, 87
lactate level, 66, 71, 72, 86
lactic acid, 65, 66, 72, 74
lateral sclerosis, 57
lead, 69
leakage, x, 76, 86, 91, 92, 95, 96, 102, 103
leaks, 91
learning, ix, 62, 67
lesions, 31, 52, 53, 89, 93
leukemia, 32
leukocyte esterase, 85
light, viii, ix, 2, 3, 5, 16, 25, 34, 40, 44, 56, 57, 58, 60, 69, 81, 93
liver, 24, 73, 88
locomotor, 54
longitudinal study, 73

lumbar puncture, vii, viii, 15, 17, 21, 26, 63, 77, 78, 79, 97, 99
lung cancer, 31, 48
lymphocytes, 22, 23, 29, 80, 87
lymphoma, 32, 33, 48, 64, 87, 100
lysis, 22

M

macromolecules, 24
magnetic resonance, 31
magnetic resonance imaging, 31
magnitude, 82
major issues, 11
majority, 28, 31, 62, 83, 84, 89, 91
malignancy, 22, 28, 77
malignant cells, 22, 31, 32, 33, 79
mammalian cells, 66
management, 46, 47, 53, 101
manufacturing, 21
mass, 20, 30, 31
MB, 56, 59
MBP, 88
measurement(s), 6, 14, 32, 35, 37, 38, 40, 44, 66, 80, 81, 85, 86, 88, 94, 95, 103
medical, 10, 28, 93
medication, 24, 65
medicine, 13, 65, 68, 69
medulla, 19
melanin, 79
melanoma, 31, 48, 79
membranes, 18, 27, 70
memory, ix, 62, 67, 93
memory processes, 93
meningitis, 17, 21, 23, 25, 26, 27, 28, 29, 30, 31, 32, 46, 48, 66, 79, 82, 84, 85, 86, 87, 88, 91, 93, 98, 99, 100, 101
messenger RNA, 43
meta-analysis, 85, 94, 99, 100
metabolic pathways, 70
metabolism, vii, ix, 61, 62, 64, 66, 67, 68, 69, 70, 71
metabolites, ix, 62, 64, 70, 71, 77, 88, 101
metabolized, 82
metastasis, 48, 88, 101

methodology, 90, 102
mice, 54, 55
microdialysis, 72
microorganisms, 78
microRNA, 33, 59
Missouri, 72
mitochondrial damage, ix, 62
models, viii, 2, 103
modifications, 34, 38, 67
molecular biology, 17
molecules, 11, 19, 76, 82
Moon, 13, 104
morbidity, 66
mortality, 66
motivation, 38
motor neurons, 40, 41, 44, 58
MR, 47, 48, 54, 96, 99
MRI, 2, 10, 31, 32, 35, 47
mRNA, 43
multiple sclerosis, ix, x, 16, 24, 44, 57, 58,
    59, 60, 76, 83, 84, 88, 90, 91, 98, 101,
    102, 103
mumps, 83
muscle atrophy, 40
mutation(s), 36, 37, 38, 42, 49, 51, 52
myelin, 40, 64, 88, 100
myelin basic protein, 100

N

NAD, 65
NADH, 65
narcolepsy, 44, 60
NCS, 30
necrosis, 10, 60
neonates, 23
nerve, viii, 2, 3, 4, 5, 6, 10, 11, 12, 14, 23,
    30, 57, 63
nervous system, x, 17, 43, 46, 63, 75, 76, 77
Netherlands, 45
neural function, 93
neuroblastoma, 88
neurodegeneration, 38, 40, 54, 55, 60, 72,
    103
neurodegenerative dementia, 41, 42
neurodegenerative diseases, x, 41, 49, 60,
    76, 77, 93, 94, 95
neurodegenerative disorders, 4, 39, 42, 56
neurofibrillary tangles, 35, 94
neurofilaments, 5, 93
neuroimaging, 35, 37, 43, 48
neuroinflammation, 50
neurological disease, vii, viii, 15, 20, 24, 25,
    43, 45, 58, 60, 63, 94, 103, 105
Neuron Specific Enolase, viii, 2, 4, 8, 9
neuronal apoptosis, 67
neuronal cells, 40
neuronal damage, vii, 2, 3
neurons, 11, 40, 41, 43, 44, 55, 89, 105
neuropathologies, 36
neuropeptides, 44
neuroprotective agent, ix, 62, 67
neuroscience, 12
neurosurgery, 91
neurosyphilis, 27, 91
neurotransmitter(s), ix, 20, 38, 61, 64, 70,
    71, 88
neurotrophic factors, 41
neutrophils, 80
nitric oxide, 57
non-Hodgkin's lymphoma, 33, 83
norepinephrine, 88
normal aging, 36, 52, 104
North America, 14, 100, 101
NSE, viii, 2, 4, 8, 9, 10, 11
nucleus, 11, 14
null, 49
nutraceutical, ix, 62, 68
nutrients, 20

O

oil, 73
oligodendrocytes, 92
oligomers, 50
operations, 13
organ, 4
organism, 25, 30, 77
otorrhea, 25, 91, 103
overlap, 36, 81

oxidative damage, ix, 62
oxidative stress, 40, 69
oxygen, 18, 40, 67, 73, 78
oxyhemoglobin, 22, 33, 78, 81

P

papilledema, 31
paralysis, 8
parenchyma, 17, 71
paresis, 8, 14
pathogenesis, 38, 40, 43, 103
pathogens, 84, 91
pathology, vii, viii, 16, 24, 35, 40, 44, 52,
   53, 55, 56, 59, 95, 96, 105
pathophysiological, 40
pathophysiology, 3, 35, 40
pathways, 38, 63
PCR, 27, 29, 32, 46
penetrance, 37
peptides, 50, 76, 93
peripheral blood, vii, 2, 4, 12, 80
peripheral nervous system, 30
permeability, 81, 82, 83, 84, 86
permit, ix, 16, 33
PET, 35, 50
phenotype(s), 37, 52
pheochromocytoma, 88
Philadelphia, 1, 96, 100
phosphatidylserine, 68
phosphorylation, 35, 94
physical properties, 25
physicians, 17
physiology, x, 17, 43, 73, 75
plasma levels, 101
plasticity, 40, 57
platelets, 11
playing, 71
plexus, viii, 2, 3, 4, 18, 19, 25, 63, 76, 92
pneumonia, 28
polarization, 70
polyacrylamide, 92
polymerase, 32, 46, 77
polymerase chain reaction, 32, 46, 77
polymerization, 82

polymorphism, 52
polypeptide, 5
polysaccharide, 26, 27
polyunsaturated fat, 68, 70
polyunsaturated fatty acids, 68, 70
population, 24, 52, 53, 65, 83, 105
positive correlation, viii, 2, 10, 65
potassium, 47, 67, 68, 70
predictive validity, 35
prevention, 95
primary tumor, 88
probability, 93
procurement, 95
prognosis, vii, viii, ix, 2, 3, 12, 15, 16, 32,
   50, 71, 93, 95
progressive supranuclear palsy, 94
pro-inflammatory, 40
protection, 62
protein constituent, 18
proteinase, 54
proteins, x, 3, 12, 13, 14, 18, 19, 24, 30, 36,
   38, 39, 44, 58, 64, 76, 80, 81, 86, 88, 89,
   90, 93, 96, 98, 103, 105
proteolysis, 5
Pseudomonas aeruginosa, 79
pyogenic, 79

Q

quality control, 45, 104
quality of life, vii, 1, 2
quantification, viii, 2, 4, 55, 83, 86
quantitative estimation, 98

R

rabies virus, 29
reactive oxygen, 69
reagents, 85, 93
receptors, 30
recognition, 17, 33
recommendations, 49, 81, 94
recovery, 31
recurrence, 33

red blood cells, 22, 64, 66, 78, 97
relevance, 5, 24, 50, 98, 102
REM, 44
repair, 6, 7
residues, 35, 93
resolution, 90, 102, 103
response, 30, 32, 36, 44, 82
rhinorrhea, 25, 91, 92, 103
risk, ix, 33, 38, 44, 48, 62, 67, 91
risk factors, 33
rituximab, 44
RNAs, 43
root(s), viii, 2, 3, 4, 6, 14
routines, viii, 16

S

scavengers, 68
SCI, vii, 1, 2, 3, 4, 5, 6, 7, 8, 10, 11, 12
sciatica, 9, 10, 12
scientific publications, 2
sclerosis, 23, 39, 76, 83, 88, 89, 100
scope, 78
SDS-PAGE, 92
secondary tissue, 64
secretion, 62, 63, 102
sediment, 78
seizure, 22
senile dementia, 21, 73
sensation, 2
sensitivity, 25, 26, 27, 32, 36, 48, 56, 63, 82, 85, 90, 91, 92, 94
serine, 35
serum, viii, ix, 3, 5, 6, 7, 8, 9, 13, 14, 15, 16, 18, 23, 24, 25, 29, 31, 33, 34, 37, 40, 42, 52, 61, 63, 64, 68, 69, 70, 77, 79, 80, 81, 82, 83, 84, 85, 86, 87, 88, 89, 90, 91, 92, 93, 96, 98, 102, 103
serum albumin, viii, 15, 24, 82, 96
shade, 78
sham, 6, 7, 10
shock, 18, 20
sialic acid, 92
signs, 31, 34, 36, 40, 67, 88
Singapore, 97

sinuses, 19
skeleton, 4, 11
skin, 7, 8
social interactions, 67
society, 101
sodium, x, 62, 63, 66, 68, 70, 92
solid tumors, 31, 47, 101
solubility, 19
Spain, 61
spasticity, 40
species, 25, 28, 35, 40, 69
spectrophotometry, 33, 81, 97
spinal cord, vii, 2, 3, 4, 8, 10, 12, 13, 14, 18, 19, 20, 40, 58, 66
spinal cord injury, vii, 2, 3, 4, 10, 12, 13, 14
spinal tap, 77, 79
spine, 2, 13, 14, 17
stability, 35, 81
stabilization, 94
standardization, 21, 94, 104
state(s), vii, viii, 1, 2, 11, 16, 21, 29, 31, 33, 65, 66, 69, 80, 88
status epilepticus, 66, 71
sterile, 77
stimulation, 8, 55, 67, 69
storage, 45, 94
stratification, 44
stroke, vii, 2, 4, 12, 85
subacute, 59
subarachnoid hemorrhage, x, 23, 73, 76, 77, 78, 97
subarachnoid space, vii, viii, 15, 19, 23, 31
subarachnoidal, 17
substrate(s), ix, 61, 62, 64, 67, 69, 71
sulfate, 92
supplementation, 67, 70, 72, 73
surveillance, 56, 104
Switzerland, 56
symptoms, 31, 33, 34, 39, 40, 86
synapse, 56
syndrome, 23, 24, 30, 86, 91, 94
synthesis, ix, 16, 25, 40, 44, 48, 56, 57, 67, 84, 86, 89, 98, 102
systemic lupus erythematosus, 91

T

target, 31, 51
tau, viii, x, 16, 21, 34, 35, 36, 37, 38, 39, 41, 42, 43, 44, 45, 49, 50, 51, 52, 53, 54, 55, 56, 58, 59, 76, 92, 93, 94, 95, 103, 104
TBI, vii, 2, 3, 4, 5, 11
techniques, 24, 33, 49, 50, 92, 93, 95
temperature, 45
terminals, 38
territory, 37
testing, 8, 26, 27, 29, 45, 46, 77, 84, 87, 90, 94, 95, 96, 99, 104
testis, 92
therapeutic interventions, vii, 1, 2
therapeutics, 50
therapy, 32, 36, 71, 79, 95
threonine, 35, 54, 59, 94
thyroid, 101
thyroid cancer, 101
tissue, 10, 11, 12, 13, 23, 34, 66, 69, 70, 71, 88
toxic substances, 19
transferrin, x, 76, 92, 96, 102, 103
translation, 94, 95
transport, 19, 20, 35, 68, 70, 71, 93, 94
trauma, 3, 13, 20, 21, 66, 85
traumatic brain injury, vii, 2, 3, 12, 66
treatment, viii, ix, 16, 26, 28, 32, 33, 39, 43, 44, 47, 62, 68, 69, 70, 72, 85, 101
tremor, 38
trial, 36, 59, 72
tuberculosis, 26, 28, 46, 77, 87
tumor(s), 21, 23, 30, 31, 32, 48, 87, 88, 89, 91, 100, 101
tumor cells, 32

U

ubiquitin, 40, 51, 53
underlying mechanisms, 16
urine, 77, 85, 88

V

validation, 44, 101
valve, 19
variables, x, 62, 68, 71, 96
vascular dementia, ix, 53, 54, 62, 67, 73
vascular endothelial growth factor (VEGF), 31, 48
vascular surgery, 14
ventricle, 19
ventricular system, vii, viii, 15
ventriculoperitoneal shunt, 28
vesicle, 55
viral infection, 23, 28, 46, 66, 80
viral meningitis, 26, 27, 28, 29, 32, 82, 84, 86
viruses, 29
visualization, 89
visuospatial function, 67
vitamins, 67

W

Wales, 52
waste, 20
water, 19, 78
weakness, 40
white blood cells, 22, 78
white matter, 53, 88
World Health Organization (WHO), 39, 56, 94, 104

X

xanthochromia, 22, 33, 78, 82, 97

Y

yield, 10, 92